Spelling Rules Workbook

A step-by-step guide to the rules of English spelling
(for British and American English)

Joanne Rudling

from www.howtospell.co.uk

Dedication

This book is dedicated to all lovers of English spelling, to all my
students past and present, and the following people
for their fantastic books: Shireen Shuster, Johanna Stirling,
Paquita Boston, David Crystal, John J. Fulford,
Catherine Taylor.

Spelling Rules Workbook
by Joanne Rudling

© 2015 Joanne Rudling

ISBN: 978-0-9931931-0-1

Published by
How to Spell Publishing

Table of Contents

Introduction

| It's never too late to improve your spelling. |

The *Spelling Rules Workbook* is for adults like you who want to improve your spelling, so you can improve your confidence in writing, your job prospects, or maybe help your children with their spelling.

It's suitable for both British and American English users.

Understanding spelling rules is one of many great strategies to learn and remember spelling. Spelling rules are useful to know because they can explain why certain letter patterns occur and why a word is spelled the way it is, which adds another layer to your spelling knowledge.

To accompany each rule, there are lists of common words so you can study the patterns. There are also exercises and word searches, which are good for developing your visual memory for what looks right.

Work through this book slowly - a little bit every day is better than one mammoth session.

Enjoy discovering the rules and patterns, and don't be discouraged if you forget them: that's natural - spelling and spelling rules can't be learnt overnight, so keep coming back to this book.

**You must work at and study spelling -
notice it, think about it, question it.**

4

Spelling and style notes

-*ize* and -*ise* (*realise/realize, organise/organize...*) Both are correct in British English. American English only use -*ize*.

I use -*ize* throughout this book because -*ize* is the preferred house style of the *Oxford Dictionary* and *Oxford University Press*. It's actually the older version of the two, and reflects the Greek origins. I advise to use one style and stick with it within a piece of writing.

Also, I sometimes use the British *spelt*. In American English, it's spelt as spelled. We can use both versions in British English.

If there are British and American spelling (AmE) differences within the text then I put them side by side. It's always good to know the differences between British and American spellings because of the Internet. Also, if spellcheck is on the wrong dictionary setting (US instead of UK) then knowing the differences also stops you getting confused if there's a red squiggle under the word when you know it's right.

Enjoy the book, enjoy learning,
enjoy the rules of English spelling.

Joanne

Spelling Strategies

You don't have to know spelling rules to learn spelling, but they're useful to know because knowing them helps you realize why spelling is the way it is, and adds another layer to your spelling knowledge.

'Good' spellers know rules and also use other strategies to help them remember spellings.

The top four spelling strategies that will help you to remember and learn spellings are:

1. **Understand spelling rules**.

2. **Use memory tricks** to help you remember spellings. These could be sayings, rhymes, seeing words within words:

<u>necessary</u> Is there one c and one s, or two c's and two s's or two c's and one s? To remember, we have a saying – "It's ne<u>cess</u>ary to have one <u>c</u>ollar and two <u>s</u>leeves."

<u>believe</u> – use the word-within-a-word memory trick to remember that it's -ie- not -ei- "Never bel<u>ie</u>ve a **lie**."

stationery or stationary?
station<u>e</u>ry has <u>e</u>nvelopes / station<u>a</u>ry = stop <u>a</u>t the st<u>a</u>tion

<u>secretary</u> – use a word-within-a-word memory trick – "A <u>secret</u>ary will keep a **secret**."

<u>separate</u> – use a word-within-a-word memory trick – "Separate **a rat**."

dessert or desert – "De<u>ss</u>ert has two <u>s</u>ugars."

3. Use syllable breakdown to help you spell long words
    ap/pli/ca/tion,   Wed/nes/day,   Jan/u/a/ry

Breaking a word down into syllables means:
- you break a word down into little spoken chunks
- each chunk is called a syllable
- each chunk usually has a vowel in it

Syllable breakdown is a good strategy for spelling long words and helps you see the prefixes and suffixes.

1 syllable: trick
2 syllables: paper – pa/per
3 syllables: computer – com/pu/ter
4 syllables: application – ap/pli/ca/tion
5 syllables: uncomfortable – un/com/for/ta/ble

It's sometimes hard for people to hear the syllables, so see words within words instead: *ar **gum** ent,   un **comfort able**, sep **a rat** e*

Syllables and syllable stress is important in some rules, especially the 1:1:1 doubling up rule and the double 'l' rule.

4. Understand how words are built with root words, prefixes and suffixes (see *Vocabulary of Spelling* for more details).

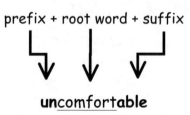

prefix + root word + suffix

uncomfor**table**

Vocabulary of Spelling

The key words and terms you should know to help you learn spelling rules.

<u>Vowels</u> are a, e, i, o, u
y is sometimes a vowel, depending on its position in a word, especially in spelling rules.

Some spelling rules depend on **vowel sounds**.

Short vowel sounds: p<u>a</u>n, p<u>e</u>n, p<u>i</u>n, p<u>u</u>n, <u>a</u>nt, <u>e</u>ng<u>i</u>ne, <u>i</u>gloo, <u>o</u>ct<u>o</u>p<u>u</u>s, <u>u</u>ps<u>e</u>t, <u>a</u>pple, squ<u>a</u>sh, br<u>ea</u>d, h<u>ea</u>ven, t<u>ou</u>ch...

(Usually this short sound is spelt with one vowel, but be careful as there are words with double vowels that make a short vowel sound.)

Long vowel sounds: b<u>ea</u>n, ch<u>ee</u>se, t<u>a</u>ble, <u>e</u>qual, <u>i</u>ce, <u>o</u>ld, <u>u</u>se, s<u>ei</u>ze, <u>ei</u>ght h<u>ei</u>ght... (They say their alphabet name and usually the first vowel is an indication of the sound, but not in *eight/height*.)

There are lots of ways to spell the long vowel sound. And we often need another letter to help make the sound:

Sometimes we add an 'e' to the end of words: *mad – mad<u>e</u>*
Sometimes we need to add another vowel: *ran – r<u>ai</u>n*
Sometimes we use the 'y': *may<u>,</u> play<u>,</u> honey<u>*
Sometimes we use extra consonants: ni<u>gh</u>t, gro<u>w</u>

We'll see these sounds in more detail in the *Silent 'e' Magic 'e'*, *Drop the 'e'*, and *the -c, -k and –ck* lessons.

Accents can affect the sounds of vowels.

Don't worry if you can't hear the short and long sounds; recognize the spelling patterns in words instead.

Vowel sounds

short	long
ran	rain
pick	peak
sit	site
hop	hope
pay	play
cot	coat / cote
sense	scene
chip	cheap
dinner	diner

long	short
been	bin / Ben / ban / bun
seat	sit / set / sat / shut
peak	pick / peck / pack / puck

Consonants are the rest of the alphabet - b, c, d, f, g, h, j...

The letter 'y' can be a consonant as in the word *yes* or a vowel at the end of *happy*.

We can have hard and soft sounds with 'c' and 'g'
'c' can be a hard "k" sound: *can, come, basic...*
or a soft "s" sound: *cinema, centre/center, advice...*
(Check out *The Letter C* lesson for more on the rules.)

'g' can be a hard sound: *get, got, go...*
or a soft "j" sound: *generous, giant, manage...*
(We'll see how spelling rules change to keep these soft 'c' and 'g' sounds, especially in the *drop the 'e'* lesson.)

Root Words, Prefixes and Suffixes

> There was a **misunderstanding** with **management** because they were **unfriendly** and **disrespectful**.

> "You can improve your spelling, increase your knowledge of words and spellings, and dramatically improve your confidence with spelling if you understand that long words are often made up of a 'root' word plus 'bits' added to the beginning and/or end." (These "bits" are called prefixes and suffixes.)
> Basic Skills Agency

Knowing **how words are built** with *root words, prefixes* and *suffixes* can not only help your spelling but also your reading, and also stops you getting scared of long words!

We also need to know what *root word, prefix, suffix* mean because they come up again and again in some of the rules.

Root word, *base word* or *stem* is a real word:

> understand
> comfort
> honest
> legal
> happy

We can add a **prefix** and **suffix** to these words to make another word.

> Can you see the *prefixes* and *suffixes* in the words below?
> uncomfortable
> irregularly
> unconfidently
> disrespectfully

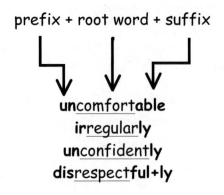

prefix + root word + suffix

uncomfor**table**
irregular**ly**
unconfiden**tly**
disrespect**ful+ly**

---

unemployment has a beginning (prefix), a middle (root word) and an ending (suffix).

unemployment

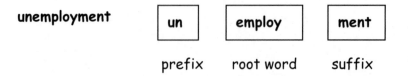

un	employ	ment
prefix	root word	suffix

The root word is the basic word and, by adding prefixes and suffixes, we can change its meaning.

If we take the root word, **employ**, and add other suffixes, we can make other words, such as **employ**ed, **employ**ee, **employ**er. Both the spelling and the meanings of the words are linked.

Linked words like this are called a **word family**.

Some root words and their word families:
use: useless, usable, used, using, user, misuse
friend: friendly, friendship, unfriendly, friendless
faith: faithful, faithfully, unfaithful, unfaithfully

Thanks BBC Skillswise

Prefixes are little words, or a letter, that go before a word or root word to change it to a related meaning or the opposite meaning: *un, il, im, in, ir, a, pre, ex, anti, dis...*

happy – unhappy, regular - irregular, import - export, dishonest, illegal, prefix, uncertain, inconsiderate...

Can you see a pattern/rule in these words?
illogical, illegal, irresponsible, irrelevant, immature, impolite, immaterial, impossible.

There are plenty of exceptions to these rules. But the pronunciation can help. Historically, some prefixes were changed to help speaking and pronunciation.

Usually write **il** before words starting with 'l'
legal – illegal, logical – illogical, literate – illiterate, illuminate...
(But *unlawful, unlearn, unless...*)

Usually write **ir** before words starting with 'r'
relevant – irrelevant, irresponsible, irrational, irregular...
(But *unreal, unrated*)

Usually write **im** before words starting with 'm' and 'p'
mature – immature, possible – impossible, polite - impolite, imperfect, immobile, immortal, improper, impersonal...
(But *unpack, unpick, unpaid... unmarked, unmarried, unmask...*)

Some prefixes have opposites:
in – ex / en – dis / in – de / im – ex

include / exclude, internal / external, import / export, deflate / inflate, exhale / inhale, increase / decrease encourage / discourage...

Suffixes, or common endings, are little words that are added to the end of a word to change the meaning or the way a word is used.

play ➔ play**s**, play**ed**, play**er**, play**ing**, play**ful**, playfully, play**able**, playfulness

With some spelling rules, we need to know about *vowel suffix endings* and *consonant suffix endings:*

Some **vowel suffixes** are *-ing, -ed, -er, -est, -ise/-ize, -or, ary/ery, -ur, -ent/-ence, ant/ance, -ous, -age, -ive, -al...*

Some **consonant suffixes** are *-s, ly, -ment, ful, -cian, -tion, -sion, -less, -ful, -ward, -ness...*

We'll see these suffixes throughout the book, and especially in the sections on drop the 'e' rule, the 1:1:1 doubling up rule, and adding ly.

Suffixes are extremely useful little words:

- We can change the grammar: *walk - walks, walked, walking; smaller, smallest; fallen, smiling, learned...*

- We can make verbs: *simple - to simplify, sharp - to sharpen, real – to realize/realise, wide – to widen...*

- We can make job descriptions: *teach – teacher, electric - electrician, assist – assistant, doctor, dentist...*

- We can make adjectives: *beauty – beautiful, fame - famous, self – selfish, wonderful, comfortable...*

Exercise

Prefixes can be used to give adjectives a
negative or opposite meaning.

Add a prefix to these words:

1. ___convenient   2. ___comfortable   3.___loyal

4. ___patient   5. ___regular   6. ___polite

7. ___adequate   8. ___possible   9. ___legal

Prefixes can also be used in verbs:
Add a prefix to these verbs:

10. ___appear   11. ___dress   12. ___like   13. ___zip

Exercise   Answers

1. <u>in</u>convenient   2. <u>un</u>comfortable   3. <u>dis</u>loyal

4. <u>im</u>patient   5. irregular   6. impolite

7. inadequate   8. impossible   9. illegal

10. disappear   11. undress   12. dislike   13. unzip

What are verbs, adjectives, nouns, adverbs?

> My **brand-new computer is** so **fast** and it **does** things more **quickly**.

Nouns are things or people: *table, chair, London, Joanne, pen, computer, dog, cat, man, woman...*

A memory trick to remember what a noun is, is to use the letter 'n' in <u>n</u>oun = <u>n</u>ame
  - A **proper noun** is the actual name of a person, place, thing and begins with a capital: *Sydney, London, Heathrow Airport, Monday, January, Harry Potter, Lady Gaga...*
  - **A singular noun** = one of anything: *a party, one computer, an egg, the man, the woman...*
  - **Plural nouns** = more than one: *parties, 2 computers, some girls, men, women...*

Adjectives describe nouns: a <u>*blue*</u> bag, a *happy* baby, a *boring* life, *healthy* person, this is *easy*

Some adjectives have -**ing** and -**ed** suffix endings:
She's *excited*. This is *interesting*. It's not *boring*.

Verbs show action or being: to **work**, I **watched**, they **are**, *listen, read*, you're *learning* and *reading* this...

Adverbs describe verbs: speak <u>***slowly***</u>, do this <u>***quickly***</u>, listen <u>*carefully*</u>, work <u>*hard*</u> on your spelling, you look *well*, don't drive *fast* (*well, hard* and *fast* = irregular adverbs)

Letter patterns

-ight, -ui-, -ible, -ough, -ate, -oi-, -ous

Letter patterns, or letter strings, are a sequence of letters commonly found in words. Good spellers know these patterns, which helps them see if a spelling looks right or not.

When you're trying to spell, you might forget the spelling rule, but you might be able to remember the pattern instead.

-ves, -ies, -os, -oes, -es, -ing, -ed, -fs, -ise, -ke...

Handwriting

Always write in **lower case** with capitals for proper nouns. It's easier to write in and means you can see the shape of the word.

Writing or typing a lot improves your muscle memory and soon you'll feel the spelling write itself.

Block capitals are ALL CAPITALS. Never write in block capitals unless it's on a form.

Homophones are words that have the same sound but different spelling and different meaning: *there/their/they're, to/too/two, bare/bear, be/bee, its/it's, I'll/aisle/isle, stationary/stationery...*

Apostrophes in words show either:

1. **missing letters** in contractions/short forms:
   don't = do not, I am = I'm, they're, she's, it's, we're...

or

2. **ownership**, possession:
   - singular owner: *Emma's car, Jon's book, Joanne's website, the country's problems, the woman's coat...*
   - plural owner: *the students' tutor, the nurses' room, the children's ball, the women's room...*

Compound words are two words together that make one word: time + table = *timetable*, hair + dresser = *hairdresser*, *toothbrush, football, armchair, scriptwriter, breakdown, handbag, newspaper...*

Recognizing compound words is useful, especially when there's a silent letter involved: *cupboard, raspberry...*

Hyphens

Sometimes we put a **hyphen** between compound words: *brother-in-law, ex-husband, three-year-old...*

Which is correct?
e-book or ebook, e-mail or email, multi-storey or multistorey, anticlockwise or anti-clockwise?

> *e-book / ebook, e-mail / email, multi-storey / multistorey,*
> *anticlockwise / anti-clockwise*
>
> All these spellings are correct. Some dictionaries have just
> the hyphen spelling, but some say both are OK.

Sometimes there can be three ways to write a word
- *bookshop, book-shop, book shop*
- *southeast, south-east, south east*
- *playgroup, play-group, play group*

Hyphens come and go in words. When it's a new word, it usually starts with a hyphen so as not to confuse people, then soon the hyphen is dropped (*e-mail* now *email*). This process has been going on for centuries!

Use hyphens when the prefix comes before a capital letter – *anti-British, pro-European* – because a capital letter can't appear inside a word: ~~proEuropean~~

Use for single letter prefixes: *X-ray, T-bone, T-shirt, X-certificate, A-list, T-junction/T-intersection, U-turn*
Notice the single letter is a capital (but not email/e-mail)

Use in numbers 21 to 99 and ordinals 21st to 99th
twenty-one, thirty-three, fifty-six, ninety-eight...
twenty-first, thirty-third, fifty-sixth, ninety-eighth...

If there are two vowels together and causes confusion: *re-align, de-ice...* In British English, we have *co-operate, co-operation, co-ordinate* or *cooperate* and *coordinate* without the hyphen. In American English, there is no hyphen.

If a word looks the same as another: *recover / re-cover, re-cover* (cover something again) / *recover* from an illness.

Exercise

Can you remember what the following are?

1. red, happy, bored, fat, tall are all _____

2. computers, phones, Manchester are all _____

3. ir, dis, im, in, mis, re are all _____

4. breakfast, laptop, waterfall are all _____

5. -ing, -ed, -s, -able, -ly, -tion are all _____

7. b, c, d, f, g, h, j, k, l, m, n, p, q, r, s are all _____

8. have, write, read, went, watched are all _____

9. parties, children, women, pens are all _____

10. L G Q M T A B D E H are all _____

11. a b d i l p q h are all in _____ _____

12. a, e, i, o, u are all _____

13. a man, a laptop, one lesson are all _____

14. U-turn, mother-in-law, spine-chilling, (-) this
    punctuation mark is the   _____

Exercise Answers

1. red, happy, bored, fat, tall are all <u>adjectives</u>

2. computers, phones, Manchester are all <u>nouns</u>

3. ir, dis, im, in, mis, re are all <u>prefixes</u>

4. breakfast, laptop, waterfall are all <u>compound words</u>

5. -ing, -ed, -s, -able, -ly, -tion are all <u>suffixes/word endings</u>

7. b, c, d, f, g, h, j, k, l, m, n, p, q, r, s are <u>consonants</u>

8. have, write, read, went, watched are all <u>verbs</u>

9. parties, children, women, pens are all <u>plural nouns</u>

10. L G Q M T A B D E H are all <u>capitals / block capitals</u>

11. a b d i l p q h are all in <u>lower case</u>

12. a, e, i, o, u are all <u>vowels</u>

13. the man, a laptop, one lesson are all <u>singular nouns</u>

14. U-turn, mother-in-law, spine-chilling, (-) this punctuation mark is the <u>hyphen</u>

Spelling Rules

Make reading this book a daily activity. Just five minutes a day and you'll soon know these rules.

1. Read the rule, think about it, do you know the rule? What are the exceptions?

2. Study the letter patterns. Do they have the same sound or are some different?

3. Do the exercises. (If you don't want to write in this book then write out the exercises in a notebook, or write in pencil.)

4. Notice the patterns and rules everywhere – in ads, in books, online. Consciously take notice of them when they crop up in your reading, and use them in your writing so that they'll become more permanently fixed your memory.

5. Next day, re-read the rule again and do the exercise.

Most forgetting happens in the first few hours.

You need to revise little and often.
*   You need to practise/practice (AmE) a new rule you want to learn within 20 seconds or so, and then review it again after about an hour.
*   Then look at the rule again after an overnight rest, because sleep seems to help memorization.
*   Don't leave it more than a week before you revise it again, and do it at least once more within a month.
*   The more you can use the rule and words in your writing, the more it will stay in your memory.

Self-assessment

A quick quiz to test your knowledge of spelling rules, and get your brain going and neurons firing!

1. Why do we double some consonants with suffixes?
   For example, *put – putting, shop – shopping,*
   but not *seat – seating, rain – raining....*

2. Why do we have double/single letters before **–le?**
   giggle but not *Google*
   apple but not *maple*
   puddle but not *poodle*

3. Why do we write **–ck**, **–k** or **–ke** at the end of words when they sound the same? For *example, luck, cook, make.*

4. Why do we keep the 'e' in *manageable* and *noticeable* but drop the 'e' with other **–able** words such as *believable* and *excitable*?

5. Why are these spellings wrong?
   a. truely   b. haveing   c. writting

6. Do we write wonderfull or wonderful?

7. What's the difference between *hoping* and *hopping,* and why do we double up the 'p'?

Answers at the end of the book in the Revision Section

Silent 'e' Magic 'e'

> **Pete** had a **pet** that **made** him **mad because** he **ate** his **hat,**
> so he gave it to **Tim** who had lots of **time at** home.

The *silent 'e' magic 'e'* is all about the 'e' at the end of words and how it makes a huge difference to the spelling, pronunciation and meaning of them: *site, name, ate, time...*

You can call this 'e' the *magic 'e'*, the *bossy 'e'*, or the *final silent 'e'*.

But the *silent 'e' magic 'e'* sums up what this 'e' does. It's 'magic' because it changes the meaning and sound, and it's *silent*! (We'll see this silent 'e' again in the *drop the 'e'* rule.)

The *silent 'e' magic 'e'* is called a marker. That means it doesn't represent a sound but tells us the sounds of the other letters in the word.

It's a marker of a long vowel sound. It makes the nearest vowel to it say its name - say its alphabet name "**a e i o u**". But we have some exceptions, which we'll see later.

Look at these words: *age, alone, date, wine, life, shine, write, volume, those, twice, marmalade...* They all have a long vowel sound. The vowel says its alphabet name.

> Notice the pattern:
>   vowel + consonant + silent 'e' = long vowel sound
>   *age, alone, date, wine, life, shine, write, twice...*

There are a few exceptions that have an 'e' at the end of the word that is pronounced: *be, me, he*

Let's look at how one simple 'e' at the end of a word can change the pronunciation and meaning of words.

Read the following words out loud. What do you notice?

tap / tape
cut / cute
slim / slime
not / note
us / use
breath / breathe
rag / rage

Did you notice the first column of words have short vowel sounds and the second column with the 'e' have long vowel sounds? (They say their alphabet name "ay" "ee" "eye" "oh" "you")

Short vowel sound / **long vowel sound**

*tap / **tape***
*cut / **cute***
*slim / **slime***
*not / **note***
*us / **use***
*breath / **breathe***
*rag / **rage***

Short to long vowel sounds.

at / ate	fin / fine	us / use
mat / mate	win / wine	cut / cute
hat / hate	pin / pine	tub / tube
fat / fate	din / dine	cub / cube
rat / rate	sit / site	plum / plume
cap / cape	quit / quite	hug / huge
scrap / scrape	bit / bite	
tap / tape	kit / kite	
gap / gape	spit / spite	hop / hope
mad / made	writ / write	cop / cope
fad / fade	pip / pipe	slop / slope
pan / pane	rip / ripe	pop / pope
can / cane	strip / stripe	cod / code
van / vane	rid / ride	rod / rode
man / mane	hid / hide	bod / bode
plan / plane	Sid / side	not / note
dam / dame	slim / slime	dot / dote
pal / pale	Tim / time	rob / robe
rag / rage		ton / tone
wag / wage		
stag / stage		

pet / Pete / Peter
them / theme

breath / breathe, cloth / clothe, bath / bathe,
teeth / teethe
+ loathe, lathe, writhe, seethe, soothe

The *silent 'e' magic 'e'* also makes the 'g' soft as in:
rag / rage,   hug / huge,   wag / wage,   stag / stage

It also makes the final 'th' more voiced and a long vowel sound:
breath / breathe,   cloth / clothe,   bath / bathe. Also in
loathe, lathe, teethe, writhe, seethe, soothe.

Other uses of the *silent 'e' magic 'e'*

1. It makes the 'hard c' sound into a 'soft c' "s" sound. These
words are long: *ice, rice, vice, advice, ace, place, mice, nice,
piece/peace*... Compare the sounds in these: *Vic/victim – vice,
Nicola/knick – nice, act – ace.*

With *fence, glance, dance*, they don't follow the vowel +
consonant + silent 'e' pattern. These are short vowel sounds
but in some accents, the *glance* and *dance* are long.

2. The silent 'e' distinguishes homophones (same sound but
different meaning and different spelling): *be/bee, bell/belle,
by/bye,   for/fore,   laps/lapse,   tens/tense,   teas/tease,
brows/browse, stair/stare, wail/whale, pole/poll, road/rode,
sail/sale, gate/gait, waist/waste, tail/tale.*

3. It's also there to show the final 's' isn't a plural: *house,
mouse, nurse, purse...*

The 'e' makes a difference to the "s" sound. Notice the
difference between the **-se** "s" and **-s** "zuh" sound in:
tense/tens, dense/dens, fence/fens, curse/curs, loose/loos.

4. In some longer words, the *silent 'e'* makes the final syllable a long vowel sound – the vowel nearest the *'e'*.

vowel + consonant + silent 'e'

divide (the first 'i' is short then long 'i' next to the 'e')

mistake

fascinate

Chinese

realise/realize

intrude

phone

quote

electrode

astute

There are some words with the *silent 'e' magic 'e'* that aren't magic!

love / glove / above / have / come / some / none / oven / cover / glove / to live have short vowel sounds.

But there is a long sound in *gave, save, clove, life, live, live wire, alive.*

All this confusion comes from the 1580s when Richard Mulcaster tried to standardize spelling by adding 'e' to words to indicate a long vowel sound, but then neglected to reform *love, come, have,* etc.

Knowing the history of spelling helps you understand why spelling is the way it is; it adds another layer to your spelling knowledge, and stops you getting frustrated with 'weird' spellings. For more on this, please check out my book: *The Reasons Why English Spelling is so Weird and Wonderful.*

Conclusion

Just one little *silent 'e'* changes the sound and meaning of a word! That's why it's so important to be careful about adding 'e' to the end of words, and also not to forget it.

It's generally a reliable rule. A silent 'e' at the end of a word following a single vowel and a consonant usually makes the preceding vowel long: vowel + consonant + silent 'e' = long sound (but there are plenty of exceptions).

This rule can help you pronounce or spell words. All these words have long vowels that say their alphabet name: *swede, rote, mule, flute, cline, hose, kale, eve...*

If you're not sure about a pronunciation of a word, you can go to these excellent online dictionaries and hear the pronunciation in British or American:
www.macmillandictionary.com
http://dictionary.cambridge.org/dictionary/british/

Exercise

Write in the correct words

1. **quit / quite / quiet**

   I _____ my job because it was _____ stressful and
   now my life is _____.

2. **bath / bathe**

   When I have a _____ I like to _____ in really hot
   water and read a book.

3. **hug / huge**

   I give my children a _____ _____ every evening.

4. **tap / tape**

   I'm writing to tell you my _____ is leaking and
   wrapped in _____ .

5. **breath / breathe**

   Please take a deep _____ then _____ out slowly.

6. **mad /made**

   I'm _____ with myself because I _____ a mistake.

7. **spin / spine**

   My _____ hurts when I _____ round.

Exercise Answers

1. I **quit** my job because it was **quite** stressful and now my life is **quiet**. (More about quit/quite/quiet in the *revision section*)

2. When I have a **bath** I like to **bathe** in really hot water and read a book.

3. I give my children a **huge hug** every evening.

4. I'm writing to tell you my **tap** is leaking and wrapped in **tape**.

5. Please take a deep **breath** then **breathe** out slowly.

6. I'm **mad** with myself because I **made** a mistake.

7. My **spine** hurts when I **spin** round.

How did you do?
Go over the rules and patterns again tomorrow.

Drop the 'e'

> Since **completing** a training course and **improving** my spelling,
> I'm **hoping** to get a promotion soon.

The drop the 'e' rule is a great little rule to know, but be warned, like all English spelling rules, there are exceptions which we'll look at too.

> Do you know which is correct and why?
> writeing or writing?
> excitement or excitment?
> nerveous or nervous?
> lovely or lovly?

The correct spellings are:
writing
excitement
nervous
lovely

write + ing (drop the 'e' with –ing) = *writing*
excite + ment = *excitement* (keep the 'e')
nerve + ous (drop the 'e') = *nervous*
love + ly = lovely (keep the 'e')

When do we drop the 'e' and keep the 'e'?

We usually drop the 'e' when adding a vowel suffix ending: **-ing, -ous, -ed, -er, -est, -ise/-ize, -or, -ish**... (with a few exceptions)

But we keep the 'e' with consonant suffixes: **-ly, -ment, -s, -ful, -ness**... (with a few exceptions)

Y is sometimes used as a vowel, so when we add 'y' to the end of words, it becomes a vowel suffix and we drop the 'e' – ease + y = *easy*, laze + y = *lazy*, stone + y = *stony*, shake + y = *shaky* – BUT keep the 'e' in *matey*

Rules and patterns with "drop the 'e' with –ing"

make – making	achieve – achieving
have – having	amuse – amusing
write – writing	believe – believing
love – loving	become – becoming
come – coming	create – creating
use – using	cure - curing
move – moving	debate – debating
blame – blaming	describe – describing
give – giving	evade – evading
size – sizing	excuse – excusing
notice – noticing	forgive – forgiving
manage – managing	frame – framing
notice – noticing	grieve – grieving
persuade – persuading	improve – improving
receive – receiving	shake – shaking
complete – completing	shine – shining
slope – sloping	solve – solving

Exceptions:
singe + ing = *singeing* (means scorching not singing)
whinge – whingeing (stressing the soft 'g')
binge – bingeing (not binging)
tinge – tingeing (not tinging)
dye – dyeing (not dying)

Both spellings are correct in:
queue – queueing or queuing; and *cue – cueing or cuing*

Keep the 'e' with
>   *be – being, eyeing, seeing, agreeing,*
>   *foresee – foreseeing, flee - fleeing,*
>   *guarantee – guaranteeing, referee – refereeing*

Also: *hoe + ing = hoeing, shoe + ing = shoeing, toe + ing = toeing*

Drop the 'e' with –ible (to avoid having an –ei- pattern)
>   *collapse – collapsible* (~~collapseible~~)
>   *sense – sensible*
>   *response – responsible*
>   *reverse – reversible*
>   *reduce – reducible*

Drop the 'e' with –ed (to avoid having 2 or 3 e's)
>   *age – aged* (~~ageed~~)
>   *excite – excited*
>   *balance – balanced*
>   *love – loved,   use – used,   agree – agreed*
guarantee – guaranteed (can't have 3 e's guaranteeed x)

Drop the 'e' with **–acy** (to avoid an –ea- pattern)

conspire – conspiracy (~~conspireacy~~)*, supreme – supremacy*

Words ending in **–ate**: drop the 'te' and convert to **-cy**

> *accurate – accuracy*
> *delicate – delicacy*
> *pirate – piracy*

Drop the 'e' or keep the 'e' with the -able ending

Drop the 'e' with **-able**

> *adore – adorable*
> *advise – advisable/inadvisable*
> *believe – believable/unbelievable*
> *conceive – conceivable/inconceivable*
> *desire – desirable/undesirable*
> *excite – excitable*
> *excuse – excusable/inexcusable*
> *forgive – forgivable/unforgivable*
> *mistake – mistakable/unmistakable*
> *inflate – inflatable*

But be careful, there are some differences between British and American spellings:

In British English, we keep the 'e' in *blameable*
but in American English, we drop the 'e' *blamable*

British English = *sizeable*
but drop the 'e' in American English = *sizable*

British = *hireable*
but drop the 'e' in American English = *hirable*

Some words have two possible forms before –**able**:

like – likeable / likable
move – moveable / movable
love – loveable / lovable
name – nameable / namable
live – liveable / livable
sale – saleable / salable

But remember we drop the 'e' with -**ing** with all these: *liking, naming, loving, blaming, giving, naming, sizing.*

Words ending in -**ge** and -**ce** we keep the 'e' before -**able** and -**ous** to keep the soft 'g' and 'c' sounds.

manage – *manageable/unmanageable*
change – *changeable*
marriage – *marriageable*
advantage – *advantageous/disadvantageous*
outrage – *outrageous*
notice – *noticeable*
replace – *replaceable/irreplaceable*
service – *serviceable*
pronounce – *pronounceable/unpronounceable*
trace – *traceable/untraceable*
peace – *peaceable*

-**dge**   We can keep the 'e' or drop the 'e' with –**dge** because the 'd' makes the 'g' a soft sound.

acknowledgement or acknowledgment,
knowledgeable or knowledgable.

judgement usually keeps the 'e', but lawyers and American English spell it without the 'e' – *judgment*.

Another exception to the rule is that the final 'e' is **not** dropped from words ending in: **-ee, -oe, -ye**

see – seeing (~~seing~~)
agree – agreeing, agreeable
canoe – canoeist, canoeing (~~canoing~~)

dye – dyeing (keep the 'e' or it'll be dying = dead)
flee – fleeing,
foresee - foreseer, foreseeing, foreseeable, unforeseeable

Words ending in **-ue** we drop the 'e' with -ly
due – duly, true – truly, subtle – subtly

According to the *Oxford Dictionary,* **truly** is one of the most misspelled words – true + ly = *truly* (drop the 'e')

We drop the 'e' in *argument* – argue + ment = **argument** (another common misspelt word)

Good spellers usually see what looks right, so keep practising/practicing (AmE) and using the words.

Exercise 1

Rewrite the words with the suffixes

1. care + ing = _____

2. use + ful = _____

3. close + ed = _____

4. shade + y = _____

5. shake + ing = _____

6. manage + able = _____

7. achieve + able = _____

8. argue + ment = _____

9. safe + ty = _____

10. excite + ment = _____

11. amuse + ing = _____

12. true + ly = _____

Exercise 1   Answers

1. care + ing = caring (drop the 'e')

2. use + ful = useful (keep the 'e')

3. close + ed = closed

4. shade + y = shady

5. shake + ing = shaking

6. manage + able = manageable

7. achieve + able = achievable

8. argue + ment = argument

9. safe + ty = safety

10. excite + ment = excitement

11. amuse + ing = amusing

12. true + ly = truly

How did you do? Go over the answers and figure out why a
word is spelt the way it is. Go over the rule, exceptions and
patterns again tomorrow.

Exercise 2

Which is correct?

1. a. argument   b. arguement

2. a. using   b. useing

3. a. writing   b. writting

4. a. noticeable   b. noticable

5. a. responseible   b. responsible

6. a. haveing   b. having

7. a. involvement   b. involvment

8. a. agred   b. agreed

9. a. lovly   b. lovely

10. a. peaceable   b. peacable

11. a. excusable   b. excuseable

12. a. guaranted   b. guaranteed

Exercise 2   Answers   (Think hard about why these are spelt the way they are and it will plant the rule and exceptions in your memory.)

1. a. **argument**   b. arguement

2. a. **using**   b. useing

3. a. **writing**   b. writting

4. a. **noticeable**   b. noticable

5. a. responseible   b. **responsible**

6. a. haveing   b. **having**

7. a. **involvement**   b. involvment

8. a. agred   b. **agreed**

9. a. lovly   b. **lovely**

10. a. **peaceable**   b. peacable

11. a. **excusable**   b. excuseable

12. a. guaranted   b. **guaranteed**

The 1:1:1 Doubling Up Rule

> I'm **beginning** to think I'm **getting** a bit **fatter**, maybe I should go **swimming** and stop eating.

> Can you remember what vowels, consonants, suffixes, syllables are? We need to know these for this rule.

Vowels: a.e.i.o.u (y is sometimes classed as a vowel)
Consonants are the other letters in the alphabet
Suffixes are little words added to the end of a word:
- **consonant suffixes**: -s, -ment, -ful, -ly, -ness...
- **vowel suffixes**: -ing, -ed, -er, -ant, -ance, -ent...

Syllables mean you break a word down into little spoken chunks with a vowel or vowel sound in them, and each chunk is called a syllable - "*qua/li/fi/ca/tion*"

Syllable stress:
Stress on first syllable: 'CAREful
Second syllable stress: vo'CABulary
Last syllable stress, which is important for this rule in these words: be'GIN, for'GET, submit, prefer, occur...

Don't worry if syllables and stress are hard for you to figure out. Use your visual memory and words within words to help.

> *put – putting, big – bigger, stop – stopped, thin – thinner, swim – swimmer, get – getting, shop – shopping.*
>
> When and why do we double the last consonant?

Say these words: *put / sit / run / swim*

Notice they all have **1** syllable.
Notice they all have **1** consonant at the end of the word.
Notice they all have **1** vowel next to the consonant

1 syllable + **1** vowel next to **1** end consonant

We never double up **w, x, y,** or **c** (we use –ck)

With the 1:1:1 rule we usually double the end consonant when we add the following vowel suffixes:

-ing, -ed, -er, -est, -en, -ish, -ery, -y, -al, -age…
run – *running,* **thin** – *thinner,* **sit** – *sitting,* **get** – *getting,*
big – *bigger, biggest, biggish, biggie*
sad – *sadder, saddest, sadden, saddened*
beg – *begged, begging, beggar*
clap – *clapped, clapper, clapping*
stop – *stopper, stopped, stopping, stoppage, unstoppable*
fat – *fatter, fattest, fatten, fatting, fatty*
hot – *hotter, hottest, hottie*
swim – *swimmer, swimming*
trap – *trapped, trapper, trapping, trappings*
squat – *squatted, squatter, squatting,*
quiz – *quizzing, quizzed, quizzes, quizzer, quizzical*
quit – *quitted, quitting, quitter, acquittal*
('qu' is counted as one letter. So the 'u' isn't considered an extra vowel.)

~The reason we double up the consonant is to keep and indicate the short vowel sound.~

Knowing all about the *silent 'e' magic 'e', **drop the 'e' rule***, and the ***1:1:1 doubling up rule*** is important when spelling and reading. Can you remember why we double up consonants?

Look at the pairs of words below. When you read them out loud, you should be able to distinguish between the short and long vowel sounds.

hoping and *hopping*, *hoped* and *hopped*
rating and *ratting*, *rated* and *ratted*
taping and *tapping*, *taped* and *tapped*

---

hoping = hope + ing (drop the 'e' but retain long vowel sound)
hopping = hop + ing (double 'p' indicates a short vowel sound)
rating = rate + ing (drop the 'e' but retain long sound)
ratting = rat + ing (double 't' for short vowel sound)
taping = tape + ing (drop the 'e' but retain long vowel sound)
tapping = tap + ing (double 'p' for short vowel sound)

This 1:1:1 rule is also used for longer words when the **second** syllable is stressed, and we add vowel suffixes.

begin (beGIN) – *beginner, beginning*
forget (forGET) – *forgetting, forgettable, forgotten*
regret (reGRET) – *regrettable, regretting, regretted*
forbid – *forbidden, forbidding*
submit – *submitting, submitted*
equip – *equipped, equipping, equipper* (but *equipment* remember only double up with vowel suffixes)
admit – admitting, admittance, admitted, admittedly
omit – *omitting, omitted*
commit – *committed, committing, committal, committee*

We also double up the 'r' in words ending with **-ar, -er, -ir, -or, -ur**:

prefer "preFER" – *preferred, preferring* (Not *preference, preferable, preferential* because the stress is on the first syllable – PREFerence)

refer – *referred, referring* (Not **reference**, *referendum*)

defer – *deferred, deferring* (Not **deference**)

deter – *deterring, deterrent, deterrence*

occur – *occurring, occurred, occurrence*

transfer – *transferring, transferred* (Not **transf**erence, transferable)

confer – conferred, conferring, conferrable (Not *conference*)

Also: bar – *barring, barred*
(Compare with *bare – baring, bared*)
scar – *scarred, scarring*
star – *starring, starred*
stir – *stirring, stirred*

When the stress isn't on the final syllable, don't double up:
budget (BUDget) – *budgeting, budgeted*
murmur – *murmuring, murmuring,* cater – *catering catered*

Exceptions:
Focus can be spelled with either a single or a double 's'
focused / focussed,   focusing / focussing

British: kidnap – *kidnapped, kidnapping, kidnapper*
American: *kidnaped or kidnapped, kidnapping/kidnaping, kidnapper/kidnaper*
British: worship – *worshipped, worshipping, worshipper*
American: *worshiped or worshipped, worshiping/worshipping, worshiper/worshipper*

~If you're not sure of the spelling, check in a dictionary~

Exercise

Which of these are right?
Use the 1:1:1 rule or your visual memory for what looks right.

1. shoper or shopper?

2. foxes or foxxes?

3. beginner or beginer?

4. fatest or fattest?

5. sleeping or sleepping?

6. forgettable or forgetable?

7. quicker or quickker?

8. planning or planing?

9. budgetting or budgeting?

10. quizzed or quized?

Exercise Answers

1. shop - shoper or **shopper?**

2. fox - **foxes** or foxxes? (add **-es** to 'x' rule)

3. begin - **beginner** or beginer?

4. fat - fatest or **fattest?**

5. sleeping - **sleeping** or sleepping? (2 vowels before final consonant so 'p' not doubled)

6. forget - **forgettable** or forgetable ?

7. quick - **quicker** or quickker? (2 consonants at end so 'k' not doubled.)

8. plan - **planning** or planing?

9. budget - budgetting or **budgeting?** (stress is on the "bud" so 't' not doubled)

10. quiz - **quizzed** or quized?

How did you do?

Remember spelling only improves if you practise/
practice (American), think about it, notice it,
write it.

Exercice

Proofread this paragraph and write it out correctly.
There are 12 mistakes

On the hotest day of last summer we went swiming in the river. My skiny friend steped on the slime-covered rocks which were hiden under the surface. He skided across the rocks, yeling for help. As he fell he bumpped his backside on some jaged rocks and ended up a lot weter than he intended. We thought it was quite funy and that made him even mader.

(Thanks to Shireen Shuster and her *Spelling Essentials* book)

Exercise   Answers

Proofread this paragraph and write it out correctly.
There are 12 mistakes

On the <u>hottest</u> day of last summer we went <u>swimming</u> in the river. My <u>skinny</u> friend <u>stepped</u> on the slime-covered rocks which were <u>hidden</u> under the surface. He <u>skidded</u> across the rocks, <u>yelling</u> for help. As he fell he <u>bumped</u> his backside on some <u>jagged</u> rocks and ended up a lot <u>wetter</u> than he intended. We thought it was quite <u>funny</u> and that made him even <u>madder</u>.

(Thanks to Shireen Shuster and her *Spelling Essentials* book)

Adding –es to Words

> She always **watches quizzes** on TV while she **washes** the **dishes** and **polishes** the **glasses**.

> Can you see the letter or letters next to the –**es**?
> What are they?

We add -**es** to words ending in s / ss / sh / ch / x / z
bus – buses, address – addresses, wash – washes,
peach – peaches, fox – foxes,
quiz – quizzes (this also has the 1:1:1 doubling up rule. But
bus/*buses*, gas/gases can double up in American English
busses/gasses too.)

Add -**es** to make plurals and third person verbs:

singular nouns – plural nouns
box – boxes
watch – watches
business – businesses

third person means *he/she/it + verb*
I watch – she watches
You teach – he teaches
They brush – it brushes

-**es** was added to these words to stop 3 s's in a row and to aid
reading. ~~glasss, quizzs washs~~

When a word ends in –**se** or –**ze,** we just add –**s**:
amaze – amazes, blaze – blazes, advise – advises,
house – houses, nurse – nurses...

50

-es patterns and words

bus – buses
atlas – atlases
gas – gases
census – censuses

crash – crashes
dash – dashes
crush – crushes
rush – rushes
bush – bushes
flush – flushes
wish – wishes
dish – dishes

bench – benches
bunch – bunches
church – churches
hunch – hunches
lunch – lunches
porch – porches
peach – peaches
beach – beaches
coach – coaches
inch – inches

waltz – waltzes
quiz – quizzes
buzz – buzzes
fizz – fizzes   frizz – frizzes

kiss – kisses
cross – crosses
guess – guesses
ass – asses
pass – passes
glass – glasses
harness – harnesses

box – boxes
fix – fixes
flex – flexes
fox – foxes
mix – mixes
flex – flexes
tax – taxes
relax – relaxes
reflex – reflexes

crutch – crutches
switch – switches
witch – witches
watch – watches
match – matches
notch – notches

Exception: if the **-ch** ending is pronounced with a "k" sound, you add **–s**: *stomach – stomachs, epoch – epochs*

Exercise 1

Rewrite the words and add -**es** or -**s** to these words

1. dish – _____

2. business – _____

3. amaze – _____

4. tablet – _____

5. class – _____

6. phone – _____

7. witness – _____

8. torch – _____

9. crush – _____

10. six – _____

11. lunch – _____

12. buzz – _____

Exercise 1   Answers

Add -es or -s to these words

1. dish – dishes

2. business – businesses

3. amaze – amazes

4. tablet – tablets

5. class – classes

6. phone – phones

7. witness – witnesses

8. torch – torches

9. crush – crushes

10. six – sixes

11. lunch – lunches

12. buzz – buzzes

How did you do? It's a very straightforward rule!

Exercise 2

Which is correct?

1. varnishes or varnishs?

2. buses or busses?

3. busineses or businesses?

4. foxes or foxs?

5. despatches or despatchs?

6. busineses or businesses?

7. mackintoshs or mackintoshes?

8. richs or riches?

9. addresses or addreses?

10. pases or passes?

Exercise 2   Answers

Which is correct?

1. **varnishes** or varnishs

2. **buses** or busses

3. busineses or **businesses**

4. **foxes** or foxs

5. **despatches** or despatchs

6. busineses or **businesses**

7. mackintoshs or **mackintoshes**

8. richs or **riches**

9. **addresses** or addreses

10. pases or **passes**

Words Ending in 'O'

> They grow lots of **tomatoes, potatoes** and **avocados,** but
> **mangoes/mangos** are hard to grow!
> When do we add –s or –es?

1. Add -**es** to *go* and *do* to make these into third person verbs:
I go - *she goes / he goes / it goes / does she?/ doesn't he.*
I do - *he does / she does / it does / does it? /doesn't it.*

2. Add –**es** to these commonly misspelled vegetables:
one potato - some potatoes
one tomato - some tomatoes

3. Words ending with a **vowel + 'o'** always add –**s**
   (If we add –**es,** we'll have 3 vowels in a row, which isn't
   popular in English – radioes x, zooes x)

   radio – radios, patio – patios, audio – audios,
   ratio – ratios, studio – studios, scenario – scenarios,
   zoo – zoos, kangaroo – kangaroos, tattoo – tattoos,
   cuckoo – cuckoos, video – videos, stereo – stereos...

4. We add –**s** to these short forms/abbreviations: *kilo – kilos,*
photo – photos, logo – logos, typo – typos, piano – pianos, ego –
egos, hippo – hippos, combo – combos, auto – autos

5. We add –**s** to the following "newer", "foreign" words:
   avocado – avocados, casino – casinos,
   inferno – infernos, tornado – tornados, torso – torsos,
   taco – tacos, stiletto – stilettos, kimono – kimonos...

   Add –s to these musical terms: *solo – solos, piano – pianos,*
soprano – sopranos, cello – cellos, banjo – banjos, alto – altos

56

6. We always add **-es** to the following words:

tomato – tomatoes
potato – potatoes
hero – heroes
mosquito – mosquitoes
veto – vetoes
echo – echoes
domino – dominoes
torpedo – torpedoes
embargo – embargoes

7. We have some words ending in 'o' that can be spelled with either **-s** or **–es**:

cargo – cargos or cargoes
mango – mangos or mangoes
motto – mottos or mottoes
memento – mementos or mementoes
banjo – banjos or banjoes
volcano – volcanos or volcanoes
buffalo – buffalo or buffaloes
tornado – tornados or tornadoes
flamingo – flamingos or flamingoes
fresco – frescos or frescoes
ghetto – ghettos or ghettoes
halo – halos or haloes
tuxedo – tuxedos – tuxedoes

zero – zeros or zeroes (some dictionaries allow -es)

Exercise 1

Write the whole word and add **-s** or **-es** to these words.

1. radio - _____

2. tomato - _____

3. photo - _____

4. echo - _____

5. memo - _____

6. potato - _____

7. hero - _____

8. stereo - _____

9. soprano - _____

10. kilo - _____

11. zero - _____

12. typo - _____

Exercise 1   Answers

1. radio - radios

2. tomato - tomatoes

3. photo - photos

4. echo – echoes

5. memo – memos

6. potato - potatoes

7. hero - heroes

8. stereo - stereos

9. soprano - sopranos

10. kilo - kilos

11. zero – zeros

12. typo – typos

Exercise 2

Which is correct?

1. videos or videoes?

2. kilos or kiloes?

3. tomatos or tomatoes?

4. photos or photoes?

5. memos or memoes?

6. heros or heroes?

7. echos or echoes?

8. radios or radioes?

9. potatos or potatoes?

10. mangos or mangoes?

Exercise 2   Answers
Which is correct?

1. **videos** or videoes

2. **kilos** or kiloes

3. tomatos or **tomatoes**

4. **photos** or photoes

5. **memos** or memoes

6. heros or **heroes**

7. echos or **echoes**

8. **radios** or radioes

9. potatos or **potatoes**

10. mangos or mangoes both are correct

This is a tricky rule so you need to develop your visual memory
for what looks right by working on the common words, or
words you need for your life or work.

-y to –ies or –s

She always **worries** when she **applies** for jobs but at least she
tries and **says** it **pays** to be brave.

We can have plural nouns: *alleys, guys, factories, cities...*
or third person verbs: *plays, says, supplies, hurries...*

Why do we add -**s** to some words and
change -**y** to -**ies** in others?

Can you see a pattern/a rule going on with the letter next to
the -y in these words?

buy, boy, tray, key, journey
buys, boys, trays, keys, journeys

cry, worry, party, baby, country
cries, worries, parties, babies, countries

Did you notice the pattern/the rule?

b<u>u</u>y, b<u>o</u>y, tr<u>a</u>y, k<u>e</u>y, journ<u>e</u>y

All these have vowels next to the -y so we just add –s
boys, trays, journeys

If we change the -**y** to –**ies**, it'll look strange with 3 vowels in a row: boy - ~~boies~~ x tray- ~~traies~~ x

There are patterns you can remember if you can't remember the rule:

- ***rays***, *trays, frays, prays, strays, sprays...*
- ***lays***, ***plays***, *delays, relays, underlays...*
- ***pays***, *days, says, bays, rays, ways, decays, stays...*
- *ways, byways, subways, alleyways...*
- ***alleys***, *valleys, volleys, trolleys...*
- *keys, monkeys, donkeys, turkeys, jockeys...*
- *jour**neys**, chimneys, attorneys ...*
- ***boys***, *toys, ploys, envoys, employs, enjoys...*
- ***buys***, *guys...*

We have some patterns around the **-ies** ending:

-by to **-bies**: baby – *babies, ruby – rubies, hobby – hobbies...*

-try to **-tries**: try – *tries, country – countries...*

-ty to **ties**: party – *parties, city – cities, eighty – eighties, opportunity – opportunities, empty – empties, duty – duties...*

-ry to **-ries**: cry – *cries, story – stories, battery – batteries, dry – dries, fry – fries, fairy – fairies...*

-rry to **-rries**: carry – *carries, hurry – hurries, curry – curries, worry – worries, marry – marries, berry – berries...*

-ly to **-lies**: bully – *bullies, family – families, fly – flies...*

-ply to **-plies**: reply - *replies, supply – supplies, apply – applies...*

-dy to **-dies**: body – *bodies, remedy - remedies, lady – ladies, study – studies, buddy – buddies...*

-ny to **-nies**: penny – *pennies, pony – ponies, bunny – bunnies...*

-py to **-pies**: *copy – copies, spy – spies, puppy – puppies, supply – supplies...*

Also, sky – *skies, daisy – daisies, army - armies*

Exception: *why – whys*

Just a quick note about proper nouns. If we add **-s** to a surname/name, we don't change the –y to **-ies** or it'd change the name! *The Jollys have gone on holiday. The Parrys are moving.*

64

Exercise 1

Change these to plurals:

1. factory - _____

2. trolley - _____

3. empty - _____

4. play - _____

5. story - _____

6. guy - _____

7. pastry - _____

8. turkey - _____

9. ninety - _____

10. responsibility - _____

11. subway - _____

12. family - _____

Exercise 1   Answers

1. factory - factories

2. trolley - trolleys

3. empty - empties

4. play - plays

5. story - stories

6. guy - guys

7. pastry - pastries

8. turkey – turkeys

9. ninety – nineties

10. responsibility – responsibilities

11. subway – subways

12. family – families

How did you do? It's a reliable rule, but if you can't remember
the rule then try to remember the patterns.

Exercise 2

Rewrite this shopping list/note and add the plurals

---

4 Danish (pastry) _____

2 vegetable (curry) _____

2 frozen (turkey) _____

Box of paper (hanky) _____

4 AA (battery) _____

Pack of disposable (nappy) _____ (diapers – Am)

Some (strawberry) _____ and (raspberry)
_____ and some (cherry) _____

2 (loaf) _____ of bread

Park next to where the _____ (trolley) are – that's

where the bottle recycling bin is so you can throw

away the _____ (empty). And could you get two new

_____ (key) cut for the gate. And also could you find a

DVD with children's _____ (story) on it please? Thanks.

Thanks to Catherine Taylor – *A Useful Spelling Handbook for Adults*

Exercise 2   Answers

Rewrite this shopping list/note and add the plurals

---

4 Danish (pastry) <u>pastries</u>

2 vegetable (curry) <u>curries</u>

2 frozen (turkey) <u>turkeys</u>

Box of paper (hanky) <u>hankies</u>

4 AA (battery) <u>batteries</u>

Pack of disposable (nappy) <u>nappies</u> (diapers American)

Some (strawberry) <u>strawberries</u> and (raspberry)

<u>raspberries</u> and some (cherry) <u>cherries</u>

Park next to where the <u>trolleys</u> (trolley) are – that's

where the bottle recycling bin is so you can throw

away the <u>empties</u> (empty). And could you get two

new <u>keys</u> (key) cut for the gate. And also could you

find a DVD with children's <u>stories</u> (story) on it

please? Thanks.

Thanks to Catherine Taylor – *A Useful Spelling Handbook for Adults*

-f /-fe to -ves or -s

> The **chefs' knives** were all blunt and the **loaves** needed cutting and the grapefruits needed to be cut into **halves**.

> Why do we change some of these words to **-ves** and some we just add **-s**?

The **-f to -ves** or -s rule is an easy rule but with many exceptions that you need to learn.

1. Most words ending in -**f** /-**fe** change their plurals to **ves**:

half – halves
knife – knives
leaf – leaves
loaf – loaves
life – lives
wife – wives
shelf – shelves
thief – thieves
wolf – wolves
calf – calves
elf – elves
self – selves
yourself – yourselves, themselves, ourselves

2. Some words can have both endings -**ves** or -**s**:

scarf – scarfs / scarves
dwarf – dwarfs / dwarves
wharf – wharfs / wharves

3. Words ending in **-ff** you just add **-s** to make the plural.
(or else you get -fves - clifves and that looks strange)
These are all short vowel sounds.

cliff – cliffs
sniff – sniffs
whiff – whiffs
tariff – tariffs
bailiff – bailiffs
sheriff – sheriffs

toff – toffs
scoff – scoffs

gaff – gaffs
guff – guffs

buff – buffs
huff and puff – huffs and puffs
stuff – stuffs
scuff – scuffs
scruff – scruffs
bluff – bluffs

4. Some words ending in **-f** /**-fe** add **-s**:
chef – chefs   *safe – safes*
gulf – gulfs   *chafe – chafes*

5. Words ending in 2 vowels + **-f** add **-s** in these words:
roof – roofs   *belief – beliefs*
proof – proofs   *brief – briefs*
spoof – spoofs   *chief – chiefs*
reef – reefs

Exceptions: *leaf – leaves, loaf – loaves, thief – thieves*

Exercise

Rewrite the nouns to plurals and verbs to third person 's'

1. leaf - _____

2. scarf - _____

3. roof - _____

4. sniff - _____

5. shelf - _____

6. chief - _____

7. wife - _____

8. yourself - _____

9. scoff - _____

10. knife - _____

11. thief - _____

12. shelf - _____

13. belief - _____

14. cliff - _____

Exercise Answers

1. leaf - leaves

2. scarf - scarves or scarfs

3. roof - roofs

4. sniff - sniffs

5. shelf - shelves

6. chief – chiefs

7. wife - wives

8. yourself - yourselves

9. scoff - scoffs

10. knife - knives

11. thief - thieves

12. shelf – shelves

13. belief – beliefs

14. cliff – cliffs

Words Ending in –ful

> I'm so **grateful** for the **useful** information you sent me – it's been so **helpful**. It was so **thoughtful** of you.

The suffix **–ful** is always spelt with one 'l'
use + ful = *useful*
help + ful = *helpful*
grate + ful = *grateful*

By adding **-ful** to words we can make adjectives:

wonderful, useful, successful, unsuccessful, dreadful, careful, helpful, unhelpful, hopeful, delightful, forgetful, frightful, thoughtful, peaceful, stressful, grateful, cheerful, fearful, graceful, harmful, playful, faithful, respectful, wishful, thankful, joyful, painful, colourful/colorful (AmE)...

(If there is a consonant + 'y' ending then change the 'y' to 'i')
bea**uty** + ful = *beautiful*, bounty + ful = *bountiful*
dutiful, plentiful, pitiful, fanciful, merciful

We can also add **-ful** to nouns:
mouthful, handful, cupful, armful, lawful, youthful, wasteful, spoonful, pocketful, bagful, headful...

Only use full when full
Full up. *Full* marks. A *full* sandwich. The train is *full*.

When we add the suffix **-ly** we get **–fully**
hope + ful + ly = *hopefully*, care + ful + ly = *carefully*,
successfully, beautifully, frightfully, faithfully...

Adding -ly to Words

Slowly and **surely** I'm learning these rules and **hopefully** I'll **totally** understand them if I work on them **daily**!

When and why do we spell a word with **-ly**, or **-lly,** **-ily** or **-ely**? And what about the **-ally** ending?

-ly adjectives: *lovely, friendly, lonely, deadly, costly, ugly, silly, likely, unlikely, lively, daily, elderly, yearly, monthly, weekly, early.* A *lovely* man. An *ugly* car. A *deadly* virus.

-ly adverbs describe the verb: *slowly, quickly, totally.* Speak *slowly.* I stopped *suddenly.* Drive *carefully.*

-ly rules are quite simple and reliable.

Rule 1: Add **-ly** to words ending in **–ful** = **-fully**
careful + ly = *carefully*
wonderful + ly = *wonderfully*
beautiful + ly = *beautifully*
successful – successfully
dreadful – dreadfully
playful – playfully
hopeful – hopefully
thoughtful – thoughtfully

But when we add **-ly** to double 'l', we drop one 'l' because we can't have triple 'l'
full + ly = *fully*   dull + ly = *dully*

Rule 2: Add –**ly** to words ending in 'l' = -**lly**:

cool + ly = *coolly*
usual + ly = *usually*
real + ly = *really*
final + ly = *finally*
general – generally
total – totally
cruel – cruelly
social – socially
eventual – eventually
accidental – accidentally
occasional – occasionally

Rule 3: Add -**ly** to the whole word:

slow + ly = *slowly*
fortunate + ly = *fortunately*
immediate + ly = *immediately*
stupid – stupidly
friend – friendly
unfortunate – unfortunately
independent – independently
quick – quickly
quiet – quietly
vivid – vividly
loud – loudly
proud – proudly
smooth – smoothly
kind – kindly
friend – friendly

Rule 4: Keep the 'e':

lone + ly = *lonely*

love + ly = *lovely*

live + ly = *lively*

de + finite + ly = *definitely*

complete – *completely*

desperate – *desperately*

extreme – *extremely*

immediate – *immediately*

separate – *separately*

sincere – *sincerely*

brave – *bravely*

close – *closely*

nice – *nicely*

safe – *safely*

sure – *surely*

live – *lively*

Also, *rarely, homely, approximately, entirely...*

Exceptions: We drop the 'e' in: true + ly = *truly,* due + ly = *duly,* whole + ly = *wholly*

Rule 5: We change the 'e' to 'y' in words ending in **consonant + le**: -ble (-bly), -ple (-ply), -tle (-tly), -gle (-gly), -dle (-dly), -kle (-kly):

gentle – *gently, possible – possibly*

simple – *simply, single – singly*

subtle – *subtly, idle – idly, wrinkle – wrinkly*

terrible – *terribly, incredible – incredibly*

horrible – *horribly, responsible – responsibly*

miserable – *miserably, remarkable – remarkably*

probable – *probably, unforgettable – unforgettably*

Rule 6: When we add **-ly** to words ending in **-y**, we change the 'y' to 'i' if more than one syllable:

> easy – easily, uneasily
> happy – happily, unhappily
> busy – busily
> crazy – crazily
> lazy – lazily
> necessary – necessarily, unnecessarily
> shabby – shabbily
> steady – steadily, unsteadily
> ready – readily
> greedy – greedily
> fancy – fancily
> flabby – flabbily
> hazy – hazily
> hungry – hungrily
> merry – merrily
> momentary – momentarily
> ordinary – ordinarily
> ready – readily
> noisy – noisily
> lucky – luckily, unluckily

But we keep the 'y' in one syllable words

> shy + ly = *shyly*
> sly + ly = *slyly*
> coy + ly = *coyly*

Exceptions: Change the 'y' to 'i' in

> day + ly = *daily*
> gay + ly = *gaily*

Rule 7: When we add **-ly** to words ending in **-ic**, we add **-ally**

basic + ally = *basically* (the pronunciation helps)

critic – critically
drastic – drastically
analytic – analytically
comic – comically
frantic – frantically
historic – historically
horrific – horrifically
hysteric – hysterically
specific – specifically
automatic – automatically
dramatic – dramatically
economic – economically

BUT not public – *publicly* (not ~~publically~~)

If a word already ends in **-cal**, we just add **-ly**

practical + ly = *practically*
chemical – chemically, political – politically

Notice how these words are built:

music – musical – musically
critic – critical – critically
medic – medical – medically
magic – magical – magically
electric – electrical – electrically
economic – economical – economically
mechanic – mechanical – mechanically
historic – historical – historically
logic – logical – logically
classic – classical – classically
cynic – cynical – cynically

CONCLUSION

We looked at 7 rules around adding -**ly**

1. Add - **ly** to words ending in **-ful** and it makes **–fully**:
careful + ly = *carefully*
beautiful + ly = *beautifully*

2. Add -**ly** to other words ending in 'l':
total + ly = *totally*,   faithful + ly = *faithfully*

3. Add -**ly** to whole words:
slow + ly = *slowly*,   quick + ly = *quickly*

4. We usually keep the 'e':
lone – *lonely*,   love - *lovely*

Exceptions: Drop the 'e' in these words:
true – *truly*,   due – *duly*,   whole – *wholly*

5. We change the end 'e' to 'y' in words ending in
consonant + le: simple – *simply*, possible – *possibly*

6. Words ending in -y we change the 'y' to 'i':
happy – *happily*,   crazy – *crazily*

7. Words ending in -**ic** we add **–ally**:
basic – *basically*,   comic – *comically*

Exercise 1

Rewrite these words and add -**ly** to them.

1. love - _____

2. careful - _____

3. basic - _____

4. true - _____

5. slow - _____

6. happy - _____

7. day - _____

8. lazy - _____

Exercise 1   Answers

Add -ly to these words

1. love – lovely

2. careful – carefully

3. basic – basically

4. true – truly

5. slow – slowly

6. happy – happily

7. day – daily

8. lazy – lazily

Exercise 2

Rewrite these words and add –**ly** to them

1. definite – _____

2. probable – _____

3. absolute – _____

4. like – _____

5. reasonable – _____

6. hopeful – _____

Exercise Answers

1. definitely (de + finite + ly so keep the 'e')

2. probably (probable so change the 'e' to 'y')

3. absolutely (absolute + ly – keep the 'e')

4. likely (like + ly – keep the 'e')

5. reasonably (reasonable so change the 'e' to 'y')

6. hopefully (hope + ful + ly)

Exercise 3

Add –ly to these words:

1. thankful – _____

2. perfect – _____

3. graceful – _____

4. unnecessary – _____

5. hearty – _____

6. argumentative – _____

7. magical – _____

8. high – _____

9. true – _____

10. day – _____

11. angry – _____

12. separate – _____

13. practical – _____

14. knowledgeable – _____

Exercise 3   Answers.

Add – ly to these words:

1. thankfully

2. perfectly

3. gracefully

4. unnecess**arily**

5. heart**ily**

6. argumentatively

7. magic**ally**

8. highly

9. truly (drop that 'e')

10. daily

11. angrily

12. separately

13. practic**ally**

14. knowledgeab**ly**

Drop the 'L'

> I don't press 'send' **until** I proofread my writing, **although** I'm **almost always** sure about a spelling, I **always** check in a dictionary.

When we add '**all**' to the beginning of words we drop one 'l'

all + so = *also*
all + most = *almost*
all + one = *alone*
although
always
almighty
already
alright (*all right* as two words is used in formal English)

altogether (Note that **altogether** and **all together** do not mean the same thing. **Altogether** means 'in total', as in *there are six bedrooms* **altogether**, whereas **all together** means 'all in one place' or 'all at once', as in *it was good to have a group of friends* **all together**; *they came in* **all together**.)
Thanks to Oxford Dictionaries online.

till
un + till = *until*

We can use '**till**' on its own.
until and *till* mean the same, but *till* is more informal

Double the 'L'

(Mostly British English)
cancelled, cancelling, marvellous, enrolled, patrolled

We usually double the final 'l' in words of more than one syllable when adding vowel suffixes. This also applies to a few American words when the stress falls on a syllable other than the first.

British: *cancel – cancelling, cancelled, cancellation*
American: *cancel – canceling, canceled, cancelation*

British: *marvel – marvellous, marvelled, marvelling*
American: *marvel – marvelous, marveled, marveling*

British: *travel – travelling, travelled, traveller*
American: *travel – traveling, traveled, traveler*

British: *levelled, modelled, quarrelled, fuelled, initialled*
American: *leveled, modeled, quarreled, fueled, initialed*

We have some root words that are spelled differently:
British: **enrol** – *enrolling, enrolled, but enrolment*
American: **enroll** *so enrolling, enrolled, and enrollment*

British: **fulfil** – *fulfilled, fulfilling, fulfiller, but fulfilment*
American: **fulfill** – *fulfilled, fulfilling, fulfiller, and fulfillment*

American usage agrees with British on *controlled/controlling, patrolled/patrolling, expelled/expelling, annulled, extolled* because the stress falls on the second syllable.

Both American and British agree not to double the end 'l' in
parallel – parallels, paralleling, paralleled
appeal – appealing, appealed. Also: *devilish* and *loyalist*

Changing the 'y' to 'i'

> **Happiness** is a **beautiful** thing but **loneliness** isn't.

If a word ends in a **consonant + y**, then 'y' changes to 'i' when adding suffixes. (But not with 'i' suffixes: **-ing, -ish, -ible** – too many i's otherwise!) Notice the 'y' becomes **–ies** in plurals.

beau<u>ty</u> – beauti + ful = *beautiful, beautify, beautician*
hap<u>py</u> – *happiness, happily, happier, happiest*
angry – *angrier, angriest, angrily*
busy – *busier, busiest, busily, business*
carry – *carriage, carried, carrier, carries,* (but not *carrying*)
easy – *easier, easiest, easily*
lonely – *lonelier, loneliest, loneliness*
pretty – *prettier, prettiest, prettiness*
necessary – *necessarily, unnecessarily*
reply – *replies, replied,* (but *replying*)
marry – *married, marries, marriage,* (but *marrying*)
rely – *reliable, relied, relies, reliant,* (but *relying*)
noisy – *noisily, noisier, noisiest*
lazy – *lazily, lazier, laziest, laziness*
apply – *applies, applied, application, applicable,* (but *applying*)
dry – *dried, dries, driest, (but drying)* either *dryly* or *drily*
ugly – *uglier, ugliest, uglify, ugliness*
dizzy – *dizzier, dizziest, dizzily, dizziness* (not *dizzying*)
empty – *empties, emptier, emptiest, emptiness* (not *emptying*)

–ay becomes **–ai–** in these words: day – *daily,* gay – *gaiety, gaily,* lay – *laid, lain;* pay – *paid,* say – *said,* slay – *slain*

Also, change these words that end in **-ie** to 'y'
die + ing = *dying* (dieing X too many vowels in a row!)
tie + ing = *tying,* lie + ing = *lying,* vie + ing = *vying*

Exercise

Are these words correct or incorrect? Why?

1. applyed

2. daily

3. compliance

4. dryest

5. paid

6. easyer

7. hungrily

8. relyable

9. necessarily

10. paiment

11. joyous

12. marryed

Exercise   Answers
Which is correct?

1. applyed X   applied √

2. daily √

3. compliance √

4. dryest X   driest √

5. paid √

6. easyer X   easier √

7. hungrily √

8. relyable X   reliable V

9. necessarily √

10. paiment X   payment √

11. joyous √

12. marryed X   married

'y' to 'i' word search
Words can go forwards, backwards, diagonally, vertically, horizontally!

```
a m r w p f d e h l o d h t d
c p u e l l g i o n e q u s e
y r p i l a u n a i w v n e i
l l e l i i e f r s j r g i l
g s i r i l a r i b b d r t p
l x r r i c a b o t s b i t p
t a e n r m a j l h u e l e a
m r e t l e t t a e c a y r b
y s r b t q m p i c i u e p u
s s e n i p p a h o h t f b s
a c b u s i n e s s n i z o i
z r e p l i e d l i t c c j l
b b u y l m d o k y l i a d y
a l i n v x l r y a x a c n y
p e i r e i r g n a x n z k m
```

angrier
application
applied
beautician
beautiful
busily
business
daily
flies
happily
happiness
hungrily
loneliness
marriage
married

merrily
prettiest
replied
reliable
said

Words Ending in –le

They have a **single apple** tree beside a **maple** tree in the **middle** of their **little** garden.

Read the following pairs of words aloud:

idle / middle
maple / apple
Google / goggle

What do you notice about the sounds?

The words in the first column have long vowel sounds – *idle, maple, Google.*

The second column words have short vowel sounds, and so have double letters – *middle, apple, goggle.*

idle and **middle**
idle has a long vowel sound so -**dle**
middle has a short vowel sound so -**ddle**

maple and **apple**
maple has a long vowel sound so -**ple**
apple has a short vowel sound so -**pple**

Both of these examples have single vowels, but one vowel is long the other is short.

Google and **goggle**
Google has a long vowel sound so –**gle**
goggle has a short vowel sound so –**ggle**

Don't get too worried if you can't hear the short or long vowel sounds just keep an eye on the patterns.

Let's look at the letter patterns with -**le** and the exceptions.

√ These consonants are used before the -**le** : b / c / d / f / g / k / p / st / t / z

x We **never** have these patterns -hle, -jle, -qle, -qule, -mle, -nle, -rle, -vle, -wle X

Long vowel sound letter patterns:
-ble, -dle, -gle, -ple, -tle, -fle, -kle, -sle, -cle

-ble	-sle	-dle	-kle	-fle
able	measle(s)	idle	sparkle	trifle
table	tousle	sidle		rifle
fable		bridle	**-ple**	stifle
stable	**-cle**	cradle	maple	
cable	treacle	ladle	staple	
bible	circle	doodle	people	**-gle**
noble	cycle	noodle	steeple	Google
bauble		poodle	purple	eagle
marble		needle		beagle
		hurdle		bugle
		dawdle		ogle
-tle				burgle
title				gurgle
beetle				gargle
the Beatles				
startle				
hurtle				
turtle				

Short vowel sound patterns
-bble, -ddle, -ffle, -ggle, -pple, - ssle, -ttle –zzle

-bble	-ddle	-ffle	-ggle
bobble	paddle	raffle	haggle
wobble	straddle	baffle	straggle
hobble	saddle	snaffle	struggle
babble	waddle	sniffle	squiggle
scrabble	meddle	shuffle	giggle
dribble	peddle	scuffle	jiggle
nibble	riddle	truffle	wiggle
scribble	middle	muffle	wriggle
bubble	fiddle	ruffle	juggle
stubble	cuddle	duffle	smuggle
hobble	huddle	snuffle	snuggle
pebble	muddle	waffle	
	puddle		

Exceptions with single 'b' are *treble, trouble, double*.

Note that no letters are doubled if there are two different consonants before **-le**.

-**ndle** pattern: *candle, handle, bundle, dwindle, swindle, fondle*

-**ngle** pattern: *angle, bangle, jangle, strangle, jingle, mingle, single, tingle, bungle, jungle*

The -**mble** pattern: *amble, bramble, gamble, ramble, scramble, fumble, assemble, tumble, grumble, crumble, humble, stumble...*

94

-pple	Exceptions with single 'p' are *principle,*
apple	*couple, triple*
dapple	
grapple	No doubling with the **-mple** pattern:
ripple	*ample, sample, example, trample*
cripple	*temple*
tipple	*simple, dimple, pimple*
topple	*crumple*
supple	

-ssle
hassle
tussle

-ttle
battle
rattle
cattle
kettle
nettle
settle
little
brittle
bottle
throttle
shuttle

-zzle (we don't have any
single -zle words)

dazzle
frazzle
nozzle
drizzle
frizzle
guzzle
muzzle
nuzzle
puzzle
embezzle

-cle and -kle endings

English words don't end in -ccle or -kkle, so for short vowel sounds we add a 'c' before the 'k' to make **-ckle**

tackle, cackle, crackle, shackle
freckle, heckle, speckle
fickle, tickle, pickle, prickle
buckle, chuckle, suckle, knuckle

Short vowel sound in **-ncle, -kle, -nkle, -rkle**
uncle
ankle, rankle
crinkle, sprinkle, twinkle, wrinkle

muscle – silent 's'

3 syllable words with the **-icle** and **-acle** patterns

article	*obstacle*
chronicle	*miracle*
icicle	*pinnacle*
particle	*spectacle*
cubicle	*tentacle*
vehicle	*manacle*

-stle letter pattern – the 't' is silent

These are mostly short vowel sounds

castle (can be a long vowel sound in some accents)
wrestle, nestle
whistle, bristle, thistle, gristle
jostle, apostle,
bustle, hustle

We only have one word with **–xle** - **axle** (It's a short vowel sound and should be axxle but we don't double up the "x" in English!)

-lle   French borrowed words: *belle, braille, gazelle*

Spelling Rules

When we make these **–le** words into adverbs we change the end 'e' to 'y'

> *idle – idly*
> *single – singly*
> *wobble – wobbly*
> *giggle – giggly*
> *bristle – bristly*
> *prickle – prickly*

When we add **-ing** we drop the 'e'

> *chuckle – chuckling, wrestle – wrestling*
> *giggle – giggling, nibble – nibbling*
> *shuffle – shuffling, stifle – stifling*

Exercise

Write in the correct –**le** words

1. When something is easy to do – _____

2. Put your arms round someone and hold them close to show that you like or love them - _____

3. An insect – _____

4. You boil water in this – _____

5. Only one – _____

6. A baby sleeps in this – _____

7. A small pool of water on the ground after rain –

   _____

8. A piece of fruit – _____

9. To write something quickly and carelessly – _____

10. The plural of person – _____

11. A glass or plastic container to hold liquid – _____

12. Part of the body where your foot joins your leg –

   _____

Exercise   Answers

1. When something is easy to do - **simple**

2. Put your arms round someone and hold them close to show that you like or love them – **cuddle**

3. An insect - **beetle**

4. You boil water in this – **kettle**

5. Only one – **single**.

6. A baby sleeps in this – **cradle**.

7. A small pool of water on the ground after rain – **puddle**.

8. A piece of fruit – **apple**.

9. To write something quickly and carelessly – **scribble**.

10. The plural of person – **people**.

11. A glass or plastic container to hold liquid – **bottle**.

12. Part of the body where your foot joins your leg – **ankle**.

-le word search

Words can go forwards, backwards, diagonally, vertically, horizontally!

```
l q u l n e l k r a p s t e b
e l g n i s p e r e c m l c o
a c e m a u j p l q l t c e t
p e g q u n v a n k t p p y t
p e p z e e k x h e c e m j l
l k t u l l g l k h o u a i e
e v y r k p k a e p n y h b s
w w o s c r y w l d i c n c e
g b a z i u b e e t l e k l t
y i x w r p s t i f l e d a j
p r g o p l d b t d k e b p n
v n v g b m y q t p e l l q h
l q g l l m l o p n e z d v w
f m y j k e a h s i t x t y b
q p k x x z f z i p r s b b r
```

ankle
apple
beetle
bottle
chuckle
giggle
kettle
needle
people
prickle
purple
simple
single
sparkle
stifle
table

-al, -el, (-le)

> The **local animal** shelter is in **critical** need of more funds and praying for a **miracle** or a wealthy **angel**!

–al, -el, -le are all pronounced the same "ul". The most common of these is –le (70%)

There is something about the shape of these words that makes a very 'strange' rule.

> Look at these words and notice something about the letters.
> *little, ripple, nibble, waffle, tickle, angle...*
> *local, animal, special, funeral, aerial...*
> *towel, cancel, tunnel, parcel, travel...*
>
> Clue: notice something about the letters with "sticks" / "tails", and in-line letters.

The letters coming before the –le usually have "sticks and tails" (b, d, f, g, k, p, t) *waffle, ripple, angle, puddle, crinkle, pimple, cradle, able, dimple, gargle, giggle, idle, handle...*

The letters coming before –al and –el are in-line letters: a, c, e, i, m, n, o, r, s, u, v, w
local, vocal, animal, personal, equal, original, central, formal, eventual, neutral, normal... travel, tunnel, towel, parcel, sequel, vowel, swivel, panel...

There are exceptions: *legal, frugal, regal, brutal, mental, vital, hospital... satchel, nickel cudgel, angel, chapel, label, motel, hotel...* But it's mostly a reliable rule.

Read aloud *angel* and *angle*

Notice *angel* has a 'soft g' sound and *angle* has a 'hard g' sound.

Words ending in **-el** have soft 'c' and soft 'g' sounds: *angel, cancel, parcel, excel, cudgel.* Except *bagel* which has a hard 'g' sound. Also, *model, gravel, camel, channel, jewel, diesel, kennel, label, level, morsel, nickel, novel, panel, quarrel, sequel, swivel, towel, travel, vessel, vowel, motel, hotel...*

Words ending in **-le** or **-al** have a hard 'c' and 'g' sound: *cycle, circle (Notice the first 'c' is a soft "s" sound and the second 'c' a hard "k"), miracle, vehicle, angle, bugle, beagle, jingle, jungle, struggle, local, focal, vocal, rascal, musical, medical, surgical, vertical, chemical, magical, logical, historical, legal, regal, prodigal...*

The majority of words ending in **-al** are adjectives: *normal, central, crystal, formal, final, coastal, medal, mental, dental, horizontal, vertical, tidal, fatal, pedal, royal, scandal, signal...*

Drop the 'e' and add **-al**: *brute – brutal, tide – tidal, universe – universal, suicide – suicidal, globe – global...*

-ul in only these words: *annul, annulment, annulled, consul, consulate, mogul*

-ol is not that common and usually with chemical terms: *control, idol, patrol, petrol, pistol, parasol, protocol, alcohol, aerosol, carol, extol, vitriol, menthol, glycol, ethanol.*

-il words: *April, civil, pencil, peril, evil, devil, pupil, fossil, council, utensil, anvil, tonsil, lentil, nostril, gerbil, stencil...*

102

Word search

```
w a f f l e a w a g z i e t z
l k m t w i e j c c x l l i c
m t i e t w r r u i i a g c b
e d u c a t i o n a l r n k y
h g f u y t a a i f e e u l z
t o j v i e l n v i w n j e e
h l r c e g f g e n o u v l n
b b a i f h m l r l t f c u a
f l z c z x i e s x g a c n l
c r o s i o r c a r r n i o e
l e v a r t n b l i i m i l n
l e c n a c r t m e a p t j n
n i b b l e r e a l m t p m u
e l g g u r t s v l i u p l t
t o s p e c i a l l a c o l e
```

aerial
angle
animal
cancel
critical
educational
funeral
horizontal
jingle
jungle
little
local
miracle
nibble
ripple

special
struggle
tickle
towel
travel
tunnel
universal
vehicle
vertical
waffle

Words Ending in -k, -ke, -ck, -ic

> **Mike** and **Mick** play ice **hockey** and **frantically** fly round the ice at **break-neck** speed chasing a **puck**.

Words ending in -ck

Notice they have one syllable and have a short vowel sound:
back, pack, sack, snack, black, lack, shack, whack, quack...
deck, neck, peck, speck, check, fleck, wreck...
lick, kick, sick, brick, click, flick, trick, chick, thick, quick,...
lock, dock, cock, rock, sock, block, clock, shock, stock, crock...
buck, duck, luck, suck, tuck, yuck, muck, stuck, pluck, truck...

We also have words with more than one syllable ending with -**ck**. The short vowel sound is next to the –**ck**: *att<u>ack</u>, ransack, shamrock, shylock, paddock, gimmick, haddock, hammock, carsick, potluck, padlock...*

We also have a short vowel sound before –**ck** in the middle of words:
jacket, package, packet, bracket, lackadaisical, mackerel...
reckon, reckoning, beckon...
chicken, ticket, wicked, snicker, cricket, picket, hickory...
sprocket, docket, hockey, Cockney...
tucker, pucker, luckier, luckiest...

We never see -**ck** at the beginning of words!

Remember, we usually double up the end consonant to indicate the short vowel sound: *sit – sitting*. Unfortunately, centuries ago they hated double 'c' and double 'k', so they put a 'k' next to the 'c' to indicate a short vowel sound, and that's why we have these short vowel sound –**ck** words.

We have some interesting compound words: *knick-knack, yackety-yak, deckchair, blackboard, pickpocket, nickname*

We also have **ack**- at the beginning of a couple of words: *acknowledge, acknowledging, acknowledgement ackee* (West African, Caribbean vegetable)

They also hated a *single vowel* + *'k'* at the end of words too. The exceptions are in foreign words: *trek – trekking, trekked; yak – yakking, yakked; anorak, Bolshevik*

Words ending in –ke
As we saw in the *silent 'e' magic 'e'* lesson, the 'e' at the end of words makes the preceding vowel long:

make, *bake, cake, take, flake, awake, mistake, quake...*
puke, *Luke, fluke, duke, rebuke...*
joke, *poke, yoke, spoke, wrote, broke, choke, stroke, smoke...*
like, *hike, bike, dike, Mike, spike, strike, ...*

We drop the 'e' with vowel suffixes:
make – making, maker
bake – baking, baker, baked
take – taking, taker, taken
mistake – mistaking, mistaken, unmistakable
hike – hiker, hiking, hiked
joke – joker, joking, joked, jokingly
stroke – stroking, stroked
smoke – smoking, smoker, smoked

Words ending in -k
Notice they have two vowels and a long vowel sound:
week/weak, cheek, leek/leak, sleek, peek/peak, seek...
oak, croak, soak...
peak/peek, beak, streak, sneak, creak, squeak...
break, steak, great
shriek, sheik...

We can add suffixes to these: *weekly, peeking, breakable,*
shrieking, croaky, croakily...

Short vowel sound exceptions: *book, look, brook, cook, took*
(These used to be pronounced with a long "oo" sound. Some accents
still say these with a long sound.)

Short vowel sound in **-nk** patterns:
ink, pink, shrink, flank, bank, sank, punk, gunk, dunk...

Silent 'l' in **-lk** patterns:
walk, talk, chalk, balk, folk, yolk, Norfolk

Words ending in -ic have two or more syllables:
2 syllables: *magic, music, static, traffic, panic, frolic, mimic,*
picnic, critic, frantic, ethic, tonic, clinic, public, graphic...

3 syllables: *electric, acoustic, ballistic, dramatic, genetic,*
hysterics, politics, semantics, Atlantic, Pacific, mechanic,
heroic, poetic, athletic, angelic, atomic, authentic, melodic,
dogmatic, traumatic, erratic, eccentric, elastic, domestic,
organic, hypnotic, fantastic...

4 syllables: *cybernetic, economic, mathematics, aromatic,*
problematic, periodic, sympathetic...

-ic to -ick and **-ac to -ack**

We add a 'k' to **-ic** and **-ac** to make **-ick** and **-ack** when we add a suffix ending that begins with 'e', 'i', or 'y' (-er, -ed, -ing, -y...). This is to maintain the hard 'c' "k" sound.

picnic – picnicked, picnicking, picnicker
panic – panicked, panicking, panicky
traffic – trafficked, trafficking, trafficker

When we add other suffixes we don't add 'k': *frolicsome, mimicry, picnics*

We add **-ally** to **-ic** to make adverbs:

automatic – automatically
frantic – frantically
dramatic – dramatically

Exception is *publicly* (**not** publically x)

But if the word already ends in **-cal** then just add **-ly**
Look at how these words are built:

music – musical – musically
magic – magical – magically
electric – electrical – electrically
economic – economical – economically
mechanic – mechanical – mechanically

Summary

Short sound **-ck**: lack, lick, lock, luck...
Long sound **-ke**: lake, like, Luke...
Long sound **-k**:   leak/leek, cloak...
Short sound **-nk**: lank, link, flunk, clonk...

Exercise 1

What endings can you add to these words?

Use **k, ke, ck** or **ic**

1. pan____

2. brea__

3. ban____

4. wal____

5. sho____

6. mechan____

7. mista_____

8. picn__

9. quir____

10. atta_____

11. gimmi__

12. shran__

13. smo____

14. ca ____

Exercise 1   Answers
What endings can you add to these words?
Use **k, ke, ck** or **ic**

1. panic

2. break

3. bank

4. walk

5. shock

6. mechanic

7. mistake

8. picnic

9. quirk

10. attack

11. gimmick

12. shrank

13. smoke or smock

14. cake or cack

Exercise 2
Fill in the letter or letters to complete these words
Use **k, ke, ck, ic** or **ick**

1. pani____ing

2. dramat____ally

3. sho____ing

4. chi____en

5. ris____y

6. ban____er

7. jo____ing

8. ja____et

9. wee____ly

10. brea____able

11. mista____n

12. mus____ally

Exercise 2 Answers
Fill in the letter or letters to complete these words
Use k, ke, ck, ic or ick

1. panicking

2. dramatically

3. shocking

4. chicken

5. risky

6. banker

7. joking

8. jacket

9. weekly

10. breakable

11. mistaken

12. musically

-ible and -able

I hope these lessons are **enjoyable** and **unforgettable**, and not **impossible** but very **understandable**!

-able and **-ible** are common patterns for adjectives.

They mean "able to" or "fit for"
available: able to be used or obtained
audible: able to be heard
breakable: able to be broken

When do we use **-ible** and when do we use **-able**?
Is it understandible or understandable,
terrable or terrible, dependible or dependable?

There are more words ending in **-able** (about 900) than **-ible** (less than 200).

-able words usually come from French.
We can make **new** adjectives – *networkable, childproofable*.

As a general rule, if we take away the **-able** ending, we're usually left with a root word:

*enjoy - enjoyable, understand - understandable,
comfortable, dependable, controllable, avoidable,
favourable/favorable (AmE), preventable, acceptable,
suitable, passable, laughable, payable, traceable, transferable,
perishable, preferable, fashionable, affordable, breakable,
expandable, predictable, profitable, punishable, reasonable,
refillable, remarkable, respectable...*

Drop the 'e' with -**able**:
achieve – *achievable*, value – *valuable*, desire – *desirable*,
removable, believable, excitable, forgivable, advisable,
conceivable, unmistakable, pleasurable, inflatable, inescapable,
measurable, adorable, comparable, debatable, deplorable...

BUT words that keep the 'e' are: *saleable, hireable, sizeable, nameable.* The best way to remember these is to memorize them.

But drop the 'e' or keep the 'e' both are correct in these words – *likeable / likable, lovable / loveable, useable / usable, unshakable / unshakeable.*

The 'y' becomes 'i' when adding -**able**:
justify – *justifiable,* rely – *reliable,* vary – *variable,*
envy – enviable, pliable, pitiable, identifiable, deniable...

Keep the 'e' when word ends in -**ee**-
agreeable, seeable, foreseeable, unforeseeable

We can apply the 1:1:1: doubling up rule when adding –*able* if the stress is on the second syllable:
forget – forgettable, regret – regrettable, deferrable...

With soft 'c' and 'g' sounds, keep the 'e' in -**ce** and -**ge**:
changeable, traceable, manageable,
noticeable, pronounceable, serviceable, enforceable...

No 'e' when the 'c' and 'g' sounds are hard, the ending is always –*able*: *despicable, applicable, impeccable,*
amicable, implacable, navigable, indefatigable...

-**ible** words come from Latin. There are <u>no</u> new Latin words!

As a general rule, we aren't left with a root word when we take away the -**ible** ending: terr + ible = *terrible*, horr + ible = horrible, poss + ible = *possible*

But there are some exceptions: *assess/ible, corrupt/ible, destructible, contemptible, perfectible, digestible, convertible, exhaustible, convertible, irresistible...*

Notice the –**sible** and -**tible** patterns. Many words ending in 's' or 't' use the –**ible** ending.

Drop the 'e' with –**ible**:
    collapse + ible = *collapsible*, response – *responsible, sensible, reducible, defensible, reversible, forcible...*

Words ending in 'c' and 'g' have a softer sound with –**ible**: *forcible, invincible, reducible, submergible, eligible, legible...*

Learn the common –**ible** words:
    terrible, horrible, incredible, sensible, possible, impossible, responsible, irresponsible, accessible, flexible, legible, illegible, collapsible, visible, invisible, edible, reversible...

Words ending in 'x' take –**able** endings:
    taxable, fixable, mixable, relaxable

Except one word: *flexible* (from Latin *flexibilis*)

The end 'e' becomes 'y' when we need an adverb:
suitable – suitably, reliable – reliably, visible – visibly

Notice that when we change the form of these words, the pattern stays the same:

verb	adjective	adverb	noun
depend	dependable	dependably	dependability
rely	reliable	reliably	reliability
envision	visible	visibly	visibility
irritate	irritable	irritatedly	irritability

The patterns remain when we add –ate, -ation, -able, -ion, -ible, –ility:

fixate, fixation, fixable
tax, taxation, taxable
rely, reliable, reliably, reliability
depend, dependable, dependably, dependability
demonstrate, demonstration, demonstrable
tolerate, toleration, tolerable
certify, certificate, certification, certifiable
operate, operation, operable
irritate, irritation, irritable
educate, education, educable
appreciate, appreciation, appreciable

collect, collection, collectible
vision, visible, visibly, visibility
corrupt, corruption, corruptible
exhaust, exhaustion, exhaustible
construct, construction, constructible

Exercise
Add an –ible or –able

1. That chair looks comfort_____.

2. The restaurant was horr_____, the food ined_____
   and the service unaccept_____.

3. I went to see an incred_____ film last night.

4. I really had an enjoy_____ evening.

5. The weather was so change_____ yesterday.

6. I hope this isn't imposs_____ and you're cap_____
   of doing it.

7. The job advert says you need to be reli_____,
   sens_____, flex_____ and depend_____.

8. The pay is quite reason_____.

9. I'm quite knowledge_____about spelling now.

10. Her new puppy is very excit_____ and totally
    ador_____.

Exercise Answers
Add an –ible or –able

1. That chair looks comfort**able**.

2. The restaurant was horr**ible**, the food ined**ible** and the service unaccept**able**.

3. I went to see an incred**ible** film last night.

4. I really had an enjoy**able** evening.

5. The weather was so change**able** yesterday.

6. I hope this isn't imposs**ible** and you're cap**able** of doing it.

7. The job advert says you need to be reli**able**, sens**ible**, flex**ible** and depend**able**.

8. The pay is quite reason**able**.

9. I'm quite knowledge**able** about spelling now.

10. Her new puppy is very excit**able** and totally ador**able**.

-able / -ible + word family word search

```
s m h x r h e u s v e n s b b
e f a q n d n e h l w o e e a
e l l n i o n i b p t t l v h
x k b b a s i i q c f i b i a
c z l i i g s t e x e c a s t
i e q b t s e l c v n e v i e
t i l r o c l a a e u a o b l
a e q p i o e b b q l b m l b
b d m z c m l l b l j l y y i
l i q o m e g f l t e e o g d
e e l b a v i g r o f a z c e
c h a n g e a b l e c n a s r
w c v v i s i b i l i t y b c
c e l b i s s o p v j d q y n
n o i s i v y v i s i b l e i
```

believable
changeable
collect
collectible
collection
edible
excitable
forgivable
impossible
incredible
manageable
movable
noticeable
possible
sensible
visibility
visibly
visible
vision

-cial or -tial

It's **essential** that the matter remains **confidential, especially** because it's **controversial** with **potential commercial** problems.

When do we spell words with **–cial** or **–tial**?

We usually spell words with -**cial** after a vowel.
We usually spell words with -**tial** after a consonant.

vowel + cial
> special, social, official, crucial, facial, beneficial, racial, artificial, glacial, superficial, judicial...

Remember to keep the end 'l' when adding **-ly**
> socially, specially/especially, crucially, officially...

We can add prefixes: *unsocial, especially, unofficial...*

Look at these words with **consonant + tial**
> residential, confidential, partial, essential, potential, influential, substantial, credential, referential, presidential, existential, sequential, prudential, consequential, circumstantial, experiential, martial...

Exceptions: *controversial* is spelled with an 's'.

Memorize these 7 exceptions: *controversial, commercial, initial, financial, provincial, spatial, palatial*

Exercise

Add either "cial", "tial" or "sial"

1. confiden_____

2. so_____ly

3. essen_____

4. ini_____

5. espe_____ly

6. controver_____

7. poten_____

8. unoffi_____

9. cru_____ly

10. fa_____

11. commer_____

12. finan_____

Exercise Answers

Add either "cial", "tial" or "sial"

1. confidential

2. socially

3. essential

4. initial

5. especially

6. controversial

7. potential

8. unofficial

9. crucially

10. facial

11. commercial

12. financial

-cial and -tial word search

Words can go forwards, backwards, diagonally, vertically, horizontally!

```
c l l a i t n a t s b u s b f
o a a m e s p e c i a l l y z
m i i j o a v p o w n r j o c
m t t l f i n a n c i a l o n
e n n m a l a i t i n i n o j
r e e c d i a c r u o f l m l
c u s o v m t z o v i g a a s
i l s d f l l n v d m k i t p
a f e p a f c d e l y c c p e
l n t i v r i n r d i f o o c
s i c u u c t c s f i w s f i
x a y c e i e x i m c s y a a
f g i w a r d t a a m o e p l
q a f l x a r d l o l l z r u
l h q q l a l a i t n e t o p
```

artificial
commercial
confidential
controversial
crucial
especially
essential
facial
financial
influential
official
residential

substantial
initial
special
potential
social

-ous

It's **fabulous** that they're so **generous**, even though they're **famous**, they want to remain **anonymous**.

The -**ous** at the end of words make *fabulous* describing words (adjectives).

-**ous** is from Latin and means *full of* or *like*: *glorious* = full of glory, *joyous* = full of joy, *courageous* = full of courage.

1. –**ous** is usually added to root words. (Some root words have disappeared over time, or only a portion of the word remains.)

danger + ous = *dangerous*, hazard + ous = *hazardous*
marvel + ous = *marvellous* (British)/*marvelous* (American)
joyous, poisonous, cancerous, perilous, murderous,
fabulous, generous, jealous, monstrous, numerous, enormous,
tremendous, horrendous, anonymous...

2. When we add –**ous** to words ending in –**our**, we drop the 'u' in the root word. (British English only – Americans just add **ous**.)

British (American)
humour (humor) — humorous
odour (odor) — odorous
vigour (vigor) — vigorous
glamour (glamor or glamour) — glamorous

3. We drop the 'e' when adding –**ous**

fame + ous = famous, nerve + ous = nervous,
adventure – adventurous, ridicule – ridiculous,
blaspheme – blasphemous, torture – torturous...

4. **–geous** ("jus" sound). Keep the 'e' in these words to keep the soft 'g' sound.

> *outrage – outrageous, courage – courageous,*
> *advantageous, gorgeous.*

5. **–cious** ("shus" sound). If the root word ends in a soft 'ce' sound, change the 'e' to 'i ', which makes a "sh" sound.

> *grace – gracious, office – officious, space – spacious*

Other **–cious** ("shus" sound):

> *malicious, precious, delicious, suspicious, vicious, atrocious,*
> *precocious, ferocious, luscious, conscious, vivacious, audacious,*
> *auspicious, tenacious, voracious...*

6. **–xious** pattern has a "shus" sound - *anxious, obnoxious*

7. **-tion** ("shun" sound) to **-tious** ("shus"):

> *ambition – ambitious, caution – cautious,*
> *fiction – fictitious, nutrition – nutritious,*
> *superstition – superstitious, contention – contentious,*
> *pretention – pretentious, repetition – repetitious...*

8. **–gion** ("jun" sound) to **–gious** ("jus"). The 'i' in these words keeps the 'g' sound soft.

> *religion – religious, contagion – contagious*

9. **-ious** ("e us") If the root word ends in 'y', change it to 'i'. The 'i' makes a separate "ee" sound.

> vary – various, fury – furious, envy – envious,
> harmony – harmonious, mystery – mysterious,
> luxurious, studious, glorious, victorious...

Other **-ious** words:
> serious, curious, obvious, hilarious, notorious, rebellious,
> delirious, previous, bilious, lascivious, supercilious...

10. **-uous**
> sensuous, continuous, strenuous, contemptuous, arduous,
> ambiguous, vacuous, voluptuous...

11. **-eous**
> hideous, courteous, simultaneous, righteous, nauseous,
> miscellaneous, spontaneous, instantaneous...

12. These two words ending in **-f** change to **-vous**:
> grief – grievous, mischief – mischievous

13. Make adverbs by adding **-ly**:
> anxious + ly = anxiously, serious + ly = seriously
> enormously, famously, dangerously, curiously, mysteriously,
> nervously, courageously...

-ous Exercise

Write in the **-ous** words

1. When something tastes yummy _____

2. When someone is well known, everyone knows them _____

3. When you're very careful you're _____

4. When there are a large <u>number</u> of things -

   _____

5. Another word for beautiful = _____

6. My office is very big and roomy it's _____

7. Another word for very, very big _____

8. Another word for worried, nervous _____

-ous Exercise Answers

Write in the **-ous** words

1. When something tastes yummy - <u>delicious</u>

2. When someone is well known, everyone knows them - <u>famous</u>

3. When you're very careful you're - <u>cautious</u>

4. When there are a large number of things - <u>numerous</u>

5. Another word for beautiful = <u>gorgeous</u>

6. My office is very big and roomy it's <u>spacious</u>

7. Another word for very, very big - <u>enormous</u>

8. Another word for worried, nervous - <u>anxious</u>

-ous word search

```
i z l v q j s q s c x m q s o
s v x i o u x u o p e a s q f
j u w y o f o n m x h w u f y
l j o i x r t c k l b c o a j
r u r d e i d s f h c j l m r
s u t g n s u o e g a r u o c
f g n u l e u o j f q h c u s
n a o q j a r o r c u z i s u
d u s k i v m r i m s k d l o
s d e o q q q o o x t g i y i
n f r q z n z r r h n g r u r
f r i v o l o u s o n a y u u
s u o e s u a n b e u n i q c
y f u t s n e r v o u s c s p
s k s n j e s q b b l r o a p
```

anxious   nervous
continuous   serious
courageous
curious
dangerous
famously
frivolous
furious
glamorous
horrendous
humorous
joyous
nauseous
ridiculous

-ant/-ance

He's **hesitant** about applying to be the **assistant** manager of the **restaurant**.

We usually use **–ant /-ance** after a word that is a 'real' word.
attend + ant = attendant, attend + ance = attendance,
import + ant/ance = important/importance,
assistant/assistance, arrogant/arrogance, resistant
/resistance, **inherit**ance, **disturb**ance, avoidance, appearance,
performance, annoyance, acquaintance...

Also, relevant/relevance, distant/distance, brilliant/brilliance,
extravagant/extravagance, fragrant/fragrance,
instant/instance, elephant, restaurant, giant...

Drop the end 'e' in these words and add **–ant/-ance**:
ignore + ant = ignorant / + ance = ignorance
observe + ant = observant / observance
insure + ance = insurance, resemble – resemblance
guide + ance = guidance, assure + ance = assurance

'y' to 'i' – rely + ance = reliance, vary + ance = variance

End 't' to 'cy': tenant – tenancy, redundant- redundancy,
truant – truancy, infant/infancy relevant – relevancy,
pregnant – pregnancy, extravagant – extravagancy

Notice the patterns in these words:
observant - observance – observation
hesitate – hesitant - hesitance – hesitancy – hesitation
expectant – expectance – expectancy – expectation
immigrate – immigrant – immigration
tolerate – tolerant – tolerance – toleration

-ant

"Dance elegant ant"

Exercise

Decide what kind of 'ant' is in each of the sentences
For example: This ant knows nothing - igno**rant**

1: This ant is having a baby – _____

2: An ant that rents his/her house – _____

3: This ant has a trunk – _____

4: An ant that isn't a vowel –_____

5: An ant that's far away – _____

6: An ant that lives permanently in a foreign country –

_____

7: An ant likes to use this to clean – _____

8: An ant eats in this place – _____

9: This ant doesn't do something immediately or
  quickly because he/she is nervous or not certain

  – _____

10: This ant is extremely large – _____.

11: This ant likes to be a _____ in contests.

-ant

"Dance elegant ant"

Exercise   Answers
Decide what kind of 'ant' is in each of the sentences

1: This ant is having a baby – **pregnant**

2: An ant that rents his/her house – **tenant**

3: This ant has a trunk – **elephant**

4: An ant that isn't a vowel – **consonant**

5: An ant that's far away – **distant**

6: An ant that comes to live permanently in a foreign country – **immigrant**

7: An ant likes to use this to clean – **disinfectant**

8: An ant eats in this place – **restaurant**

9: This ant doesn't do something immediately or quickly because he/she is nervous or not certain – **hesitant**

10: This ant is extremely large – **giant**

11: This ant likes to be a **contestant** in contests.

-ent / -ence

> Stud**ents** are cont**ent** to sleep in t**ents** to be independ**ent**.
> It's appar**ent** you have to be confid**ent** and independ**ent** to make a c**ent**.

Use **-ent / -ence** usually after a word that has no meaning:
confid + ent = confident, confid + ence = confidence,
intellig + ent/ence = intelligent/intelligence,
different/difference, competent/competence,
influence, frequent/frequency, consequence, experience...

Some **-ent** letter patterns:

-cent: *accent, scent, recent, crescent, decent, translucent, innocent/innocence, per cent (percent – American)*

-dent: *accident, incident, student, confident/confidence, evident/evidence, independent/independence, resident/residence, correspondent/correspondence...*

-cient ("shunt" sound): *ancient, efficient, inefficient, sufficient, insufficient...*

-tient ("shun" sound): *patient, patience, impatient/impatience...*

-ient: *client, resilient/resilience, convenient/convenience, inconvenient/inconvenience, obedient/obedience...*

-lent: *silent/silence, excellent/excellence, violent/violence equivalent/equivalence, prevalent/prevalence, succulent, talent, turbulent/turbulence...*

-nent: *permanent, component, continent, prominent...*

End 't' to '**cy**'
decent – decency, resident – residency, current – currency, complacent – complacency, efficient – efficiency...

132

-ent or -ant Exercise

Add an 'e' or 'a' to these words.

1. arrog__nt

2. appear__nce

3. independ__nt

4. resid__nt

5. effici__nt

6. perman__nt

7. pregn__ncy

8. confid__nce

9. inconveni__nt

10. acquaint__nce

11. pati__nt

12. guid__nce

-ent or -ant Exercise Answers

Add an 'e' or 'a' to these words.

1. arrogant

2. appearance

3. independent

4. resident

5. efficient

6. permanent

7. pregnancy

8. confidence

9. inconvenient

10. acquaintance

11. patient

12. guidance

-tion, -sion, -cian

> They **mentioned** that on this **occasion** the **competition** to get the **promotion** was hard because of the **recession**.

These "shun" endings are nouns, and sound the same, or slightly similar, which can cause problems spelling them.

-**tion** is the most common ending:

1. Add -**ion** to words ending in 't':
   act – *action, interrupt – interruption, prevent – prevention, exception, insertion, exhaustion, suggestion, congestion...*
   -*ct* + *ion*: *reject* – *rejection, protect – protection, injection, instruction, inspection, correction...*

2. With words ending in 'te' drop the 'e' and add –**ion**:
   educate – *education, congratulate – congratulations, fascinate – fascination, complete – completion, relate – relation, accommodate – accommodation, separate – separation, populate – population, communicate – communication...*

3. We add -**ation** to make the pronunciation easier:
   present – *presentation, confront – confrontation, expect – expectation, tempt – temptation, plant – plantation...*

4. In some words we drop the 'e' and add –**ation**:
   invite – *invitation, inspire – inspiration, declare – declaration, prepare – preparation, combination, perspiration, compilation, determination, examination, inclination, exploration...*

5. In some words we drop the 'e' and add –**ition**:
   compete – *competition, define – definition, pose – position, composition, opposition, decomposition, exposition...*

6. In some words we change the 'y' to 'i' and add –**cation**:
   apply – *application, certify – certification, qualify – qualification, justification, identification, multiplication...*

-sion Not that many nouns end in **-sion**.

1. They're often formed from verbs ending in **-d, -de, -se, -t**
Drop the 'de' or 'd' and add **-sion**: *collide – collision, explode – explosion, persuade – persuasion, conclude – conclusion, division, expansion, suspension, comprehension...*

Drop the 'e' and add **-ion**: revise – revision, *infuse – infusion, televise – television, convulse – convulsion, repulse – repulsion...*

Also: occasion, pension, expulsion

2. **-ssion** endings. When words end in **-ss** just add **–ion**.
discuss - discussion, confess - confession, obsess - obsession, impression, depression, succession, possession, expression, oppression, compression, digression, aggression, recession, profession, procession... Also: *mission, passion, session*

3. **-mit** to **–ssion** – we drop the **–t** and add **–ssion**:
admit – admission, permit – permission, omit – omission, commit – commission, remit – remission transmit – transmission, submit – submission...

4. **-cede / -ceed** to **–ssion**: *succeed – succession, proceed – procession, concede – concession, recede – recession...*

-cian endings usually mean occupation, profession, or job:
optician, politician, musician, beautician, dietician, electrician, technician, clinician, magician, statistician, mathematician...

-tian endings usually mean place of origin or a belief: *Martian, Dalmatian, Christian, Faustian, Alsatian, Croatian*

–cion ending just has two common nouns:
suspicion and *coercion*

Exercise

Rewrite these words and change them to a noun or job
with **-ion, -tion, -sion, -ssion** or **-cian** ending.

1. obsess - _____

2. electric - _____

3. accommodate - _____

4. beauty - _____

5. discuss - _____

6. admit - _____

7. televise - _____

8. express - _____

9. invite - _____

10. music - _____

11. reject - _____

12. compete - _____

Exercise Answers

Rewrite these words and change them to a noun or job with **-ion, -tion, -sion, -ssion** or **-cian** ending.

1. obsess – <u>obsession</u>

2. electric - <u>electrician</u>

3. accommodate - <u>accommodation</u>

4. beauty - <u>beautician</u>

5. discuss - <u>discussion</u>

6. admit - <u>admission</u>

7. televise - <u>television</u>

8. express - <u>expression</u>

9. invite - <u>invitation</u>

10. music - <u>musician</u>

11. reject - <u>rejection</u>

12. compete - <u>competition</u>

The Letter 'c' - its sounds, rules and history

"The letter C is no letter at all." – John Baret, 1580.

> When it's **cold**, I like drinking **cappuccino**, e**s**pecially in a **cosy café** in the **city centre/center**.

The letter **C** is a problem letter that has been talked about over the centuries.

Its sound can be **"k"**, **"s"**, **"ch"**, **"sh"**, **"q - cue"** or **silent**:
can, city, cheese, champagne, cue, muscle.

We have a few rules:

A soft '**c**' ("s" sound) before **e, i** or **y** - *cell, city, cyber, citizen, grace, cinema, decide, celebrate, cemetery, cent, cease, cinch, cyst, cigarette, cylinder, centre/center, decide, acceptance, procession, precision, cymbal, cynic...*

Remember, *serviceable, noticeable, etc.* (Keep the 'e' so that the 'c' remains soft.)

A hard 'c' ("k" sound) before **a, o, u,** or a **consonant** – *can, cod, cut, class, curve, curb, cough, back, colour/color, coin, core, coast, Canada, claim, acre, crumb, could, custom, coffee, curl, culprit, uncle, account, academic, acoustic, uncaring...*

A hard 'c' if it's the final letter – *public, traffic, picnic, panic...*

Remember, *despicable, applicable, etc.* (Drop the 'e' to keep the hard 'c'.)

When two c's are together, the rule still applies.
-**cc**- (The first 'c' is hard and the second soft before **e, i, y**) – *accept, accent, success, accident, eccentric*... (but *soccer*)

-**cc**- ("k" sound for both c's before **a, o, u,** or a **consonant**) – *account, accommodate, occasion, ecclesiastic, accolade, accurate, occupy (these last two have a "k" + "q" sound)*

c- ("ch" sound for Italian borrowed words) *cello, vermicelli, cappuccino, concerto*

-**c**- ("sh" sound with 'ci' and 'ce') *special, ocean, gracious, liquorice/licorice (AmE), physician...*

silent 'c' – *muscle, science, indict, scent, scissors, scene...*

"q" ("cue" sound) – *cue, cure, acute, curiosity, cube, Cuba, cubic,* cumulative, cumulus, accumulate, *cucumber (has a "q" sound on the first 'c', and a hard 'c' on the second)*

Some words have both sounds: bi**cycle**, *cycle, cybernetics, reconcile* (hard "c" before 'o', and soft 'c' before 'i')

British and American differences:
> *kerb* (British) vs. *curb* (American)
> *disk* (British) vs. *disc* (American)
> *sceptic* (British) vs. *skeptic* (American)

Since the 1700s, the "q", "k", "s" sounds are or have been used for Islam's holy book – *Coran, Koran* to *Quran* or *Qur'an.*

When adding –**ing, -ed, -er** or –**y** to words ending in –**ic**, we must add 'k' to keep the hard 'c' sound: picnic – *picnicking/ picnicked/picnicker,* panic – *panicked/panicking/ panicky, traffic – trafficking/trafficked...*

Exercise

Fill in the letters that come after C.

A C__nadian woman who has smoked for 95 years has finally

dec__ded to give up. **Lucy Cooper announc__d** she would

c__t out all c__garettes as she c__lebrated her 105th

birthday today. Mrs Cooper has always c__aimed that she is

not **addic__ed** to **tobacc__** and c__uld stop at any time.

Now, she says the time has c__me. "I paid about 10 c__nts

for a **pac__et** when I started, and look at the **pric__** now!

We used to smoke in the c__nema and teachers even smoked

in the c__ass, but there aren't many **plac__s** you c__n smoke

in **public** now. The c__ilings in my apartment are brown and

my c__othes smell. I'm quitting!"

Thanks to Johanna Stirling for this exercise in her great book:
Teaching Spelling to English Language Learners.

Exercise Answers

A **Canadian** woman who has smoked for 95 years has finally **decided** to give up. **Lucy Cooper announced** she would **cut** out all **cigarettes** as she **celebrated** her 105th birthday today.

Mrs Cooper has always **claimed** that she is not **addicted** to **tobacco** and **could** stop at any time. Now, she says the time has **come**. "I paid about 10 **cents** for a **packet** when I started, and look at the **price** now! We used to smoke in the **cinema** and teachers even smoked in the **class**, but there aren't many **places** you **can** smoke in **public** now. The **ceilings** in my apartment are brown and my **clothes** smell. I'm quitting!"

Thanks to Johanna Stirling for this exercise in her great book: *Teaching Spelling to English Language Learners.*

'ie' or 'ei'

> I **received eight pieces** of paper as a **receipt** for a **beige** coat I bought my **niece.**

There are 7 sounds for 'ie' and 'ei' patterns:

1. the "ee" sound as in "green" (*relief, field, receive*)
2. the "ay" sound as in "pay" (*weigh, eight, vein*)
3. the "i" sound as in "hit" (*foreign, counterfeit*)
4. the "eye" sound as in "ice" (*height, feisty*)
5. the "eh" sound as in "best" (*leisure, friend*)
6. the "uh" sound as in "hunt" (*patient, ancient*)
7. the "oo" sound as in "shoe" (*view, in lieu*)

We have a popular saying to help us remember these:
"i before e except after c"

But this doesn't cover the exceptions. A longer version is *'i before e except after a long c or when sounded like "ay" in neighbour and weigh'*

or *'i before e except after c, but not when c is a "sh" sound or when sounded like "ay" in neighbour or weigh'*

A bit tricky to remember these, but they're reliable.

1. –ie– (the long "ee" sound)

The famous "i before e except after c" rule applies to this sound but it needs an extra bit added:

> "i before e except after c *when it's a long c*"
> belief   receive

There are exceptions to this rule so be careful.

–ie– patterns
"i before e" applies to the following common words:

-ief	-ieve	-ield	-iece
belief	achieve	field	piece
brief	believe	yield	apiece
briefly	grieve	shield	niece
chief	reprieve	wield	
grief	retrieve		**-ierce**
relief	thieve		fierce
thief	relieve		pierce
mischief	relieved		
	achieving		
	achievement		

Also: *priest, siege, hygiene, cashier, pier, shriek, diesel*

Spelling rules: drop the 'e': *achieve – achieving, achieved; believe – believing, believed, believer; relieve – relieving, relieved; retrieve – retrieving, retrieval; grieve – grieving, grieved; thieve – thieving, thieved...*
(-f to –vous) mischief – *mischievous, mischievously, mischievousness.*

> You can also use a word-within-a-word memory trick to help. Can you see the words hidden in *piece, believe, relief?*

144

> See words within words, and use sayings and rhymes to help you remember the difficult **ie** pattern:
> A **pie**ce of **pie**. Never bel**ie**ve a **lie**. It's a rel**ie**f to **lie** down.

-cei- pattern "i before e **except** after a long c"

c + ei = "cee"	**-ceive**
ceiling	receive
conceit	conceive
deceit	deceive
receipt	perceive
	deceive

Drop the 'e' with –ing/-ed/-er/-able
receiving / received /receiver
deceiving / deceived /deceiver
conceiving / conceived / conceivable/
inconceivable

(exception: *species*)

Exceptions: **-cie-** ("shu" or "s" sounds)
ancient, science, society, efficient

Exceptions: -ei- with a long "ee" and not after 'c'.
either, neither (or pronounced with "eye" sound)
protein, caffeine
seize, seizure
Sheila, Keith
weird

2. **-ei-** (the "ay" sound as in "say", "eight")

eight	weigh	beige
freight	weight	veil
weight	neighbour	rein
eighty	neighbor (AmE)	reindeer
eighteen	surveillance	reign/reigns
		vein
		chow mein

"i before **e** except after **c** or when sounded like '*a*' as in *neighbour* & *weigh*"
neighbor (American English)

3. **-ei-** (the short "i" sound as in "hit" "bit")

counterfeit
foreign
forfeit
sovereign

but different sound in *reign/reigns* see above

Exceptions: *series, sieve,* (*handkerchief* and *mischief* can be pronounced with a long "e" or short "i)

4. **-ei-** (the long i "eye" sound as in "nice")

eiderdown	height	Fahrenheit
*either	sleight	Rottweiler
*neither		poltergeist
heist		apartheid
feisty		zeitgeist
seismic		kaleidoscope

Exceptions: *died, tied, lied, hierarchy*
*either/neither can be a long "ee" sound too.

5. **-ei-** or **-ie-** (The "eh" sound as in "left"/"best")

-ie- *friend, friendly, friendliness*
-ei- in **leisure, leisurely, leisureliness*
(*some American accents say these with a long "ee" sound.)

6. **-ie-** (the "shu" sound as in "hunt"/ "shunt"

ancient	conscience	patient
proficient		patience
efficient		
inefficient		

"*i* before *e* except after *c* but not when *c* is a sh sound"

7. -**ie**- (the "oo" or "yew" sound)

in lieu,   view,   review

8. Separate sounds

In the previous 7 sounds, they are single sounds.

The 'i' and 'e' are sound separately in the following words:

variety	reinforce	reincarnate
gaiety	reiterate	spontaneity
premier	copier	quiet
crier	drier	driest
science	scientist	conscientious
glacier	fiery	

The memory trick sayings:

"i before e except after a long c, but not after a c that sounds like 'sh'"

"i before e except after a long c or when sounded like "ay" in neighbour /neighbor and weigh"

Exercise 1

Which one is correct? And why? Does it follow a rule?

1. a. recieve b. receive

2. a. ancient b. anceint

3. a. friend b. freind

4. a. hieght b. height

5. a. reciept b. receipt

6. a. patient b. pateint

7. a. peice b. piece

8. a. believe b. beleive

9 a. relief b. releif

10. a. conceieve b. conceive

Exercise 1   Answers

Which one is correct? Ask yourself why? Does it follow a rule?

1. a. ~~recieve~~   b. receive

2. a. ancient   b. ~~anceint~~

3. a. friend   b. ~~freind~~

4. a. ~~hieght~~   b. height

5. a. ~~reciept~~   b. receipt

6. a. patient   b. ~~pateint~~

7. a. ~~peice~~   b. piece

8. a. believe   b. ~~beleive~~

9. a. relief   b. ~~releif~~

20. a. ~~conceieve~~   b. conceive

Exercise 2

Fill in with either -ie- or -ei-

1. ach___ve

2. bel___ve

3. ch___f

4. pat___nce

5. for___gn

6. ___ther

7. w___gh

8. ___ght

9. rec___ve

10. conc___t

11. qu___t

12. n___ghbour (or n___ghbor American)

Exercise 2   Answers

Fill in either -ie- or -ei-

1. achieve

2. believe

3. chief

4. patience

5. foreign

6. either

7. weigh

8. eight

9. receive

10. conceit

11. quiet

12. neighbour (or neighbor AmE)

Silent Letter Rules

> I **know** your **daughter** is a **plumber**; **would** it be OK to call her **tonight** to fix my **two** taps?

Silent letters are the letters in words that are not pronounced but make a huge difference to the meaning and sometimes the pronunciation of the word.

More than 60% of English words have silent letters in them, which can cause all sorts of problems spelling the word or looking for the word in a dictionary, and reading the word.

Silent letters aren't there to mess with your brain or make spelling and reading hard – honest. They're there for various reasons. They perform a lot of functions, so understanding these reasons will definitely help your spelling, reading, pronunciation and confidence.

Most silent letters used to be pronounced but are left in the words to show the history of the word.

Some academics over the centuries chose to put silent letters in words to make the word more like their classical Latin and Greek roots: *debt, doubt, receipt.*

Silent letters are very useful:

1. A silent letter can help us work out the meaning of a word, and it can also change the pronunciation, even though it's silent: *sin / sign, rat / rate*

Sometimes a letter can be silent in one word but not in others. These letters help to connect different forms of the same word, for example, *resign / resignation, sign / signal, crumb/crumble, bomb/bombard, muscle/muscular, debt/debit, Christmas/Christ, fasten/fast, limb/limber.* This is probably because it makes the pronunciation easier.

2. Silent letters help the reader to distinguish between homophones, which are words that have the same sound but a different meaning and different spelling: *in/inn, be/bee, to/too/two, know/no, whole/hole, knot/not, hour/our...*

3. We saw in the *magic 'e' silent 'e'* lesson that if we add a silent 'e' to the end of short vowel sounding words, it usually makes the word into a long vowel sound: *rid/ride, cop/cope, hat/hate, tap/tape, at/ate...*

4. Some words with silent letters in them are loanwords from other languages: silent 'h' in *khaki*, silent 's' in *fracas*, silent 'g' in *champagne*.

5. Silent letters help to show "hard" consonants: the silent 'u' in *guest, guide, guy, guess, guard.* Without the 'u', the letter 'g' would make the soft "j" sound.

6. Silent letters show the history and origins of words:

Plumber is a Roman/Latin word from the Roman word for lead pipe, *plumbum.*

Knife, knock, know, gnat, gnaw are all Viking words that used to be pronounced but not now; but we leave the letters in there to see the origin and history of the word.

The history of –**gh**-

The difficult -**gh** letter patterns: –**ight, -gh-, -gh, -ough**, all come from Anglo-Saxon words (in brackets): *daughter* (dohtor), *night* (niht), *light* (liht), *bright* (beorht), *dough* (dāg), *bough* (bōh).

1: In the Anglo-Saxon words above, the 'h' was a hard, throaty sound like the Scottish sound in *loch.*

2: Then around the 13th century, the 'h' became 'gh' because of the French influence to try to indicate this throaty sound.

3: Then in about the 17th century, the 'gh' sound was either dropped or became an 'f' sound: *enough, cough, though, through, plough, rough, borough, slaughter, laugh...*

There's an 'f' sound in some of these words because they were pronounced with an 'f' sound originally in some counties.

-**ough** has seven sounds:

"Have you thought this through thoroughly enough?"

oo – "too"   *through*

off – "coff" *cough, trough*

uff – "cuff" *enough, rough, tough*

oh – "toe" *dough, though, although*

ow – "how" *bough, doughty*

u – "uh, up" *borough, thorough*

or – "or" *bought, brought, fought, ought, sought, thought*

-**augh** normally sounds like "or" – *"door/nor"*

daughter, naughty, slaughter, taught, haughty

but *laugh* is pronounced with a long or short 'a'

-**eigh** normally sounds like "ay" – *"say, day"*

eight, neighbour/neighbor (AmE), weigh, weight, sleigh

but *height* rhymes with *bite*!!

-**igh** sounds like "eye" - *"tie/fly"*

high, sigh, thigh, light, delight, sight, might, night, right, tight, flight

Patterns & Rules

kn- silent **k** before **n**: _kn̲ee, know, knife, knives, knob, knot, knuckle, knock, knack, knave, knead, kneel, knew, knickerbocker, knight knit..._ K used to be pronounced but in the 17th century began to drop out of fashion.

gn- silent **g** before **n**: _gnat, gnaw, gnash, gnarl, gnome..._
-gn- a_lign, assign, benign, design, malign, reign, sign, campaign, poignant, champagne, cologne, foreign..._

wr- silent **w** before **r**: _wr̲ite, wrist, wrinkle, wring, wriggle, wrong, wrote, wrap, wrangle, wrath, wreck, wrench, wretched, wry, awry, playwright, wrestle_ (silent _w, t, e!_)

ps- silent **p** before **s**: _p̲sychic, psalm, psychology, psychiatry..._
These words have Greek origins.

-lk silent **l** before **k**: _fol̲k, walk, talk, yolk, chalk..._

-mb- silent **b** after **m**: _plum̲b̲er, numb, dumb, thumb, crumb, climb, limb, lamb, succumb, bomb, comb, tomb, womb..._

-mn silent **n** after **m**: _autum̲n̲, column, solemn, condemn, hymn, damn..._

-lm- silent **l** before **m**: _palm, calm, psalm_ (silent p & l), _qualm, alms, almond, balm, salmon..._

-st- silent **t** after **s**: _lis̲t̲en, fasten, glisten, moisten, hasten, chasten, christen..._
-stle _bristle, bustle, castle, gristle, hustle, jostle, mistletoe, rustle, thistle, whistle, wrestle_ (silent w/t)

Silent letters in some common words, surnames, names and places:

A – artistic**a**lly, dramatic**a**lly, logic**a**lly, music**a**lly...

B – clim**b**, com**b**, crum**b**, thumb, numb, su**b**tle, de**b**t, dou**b**t

C – a**c**quire, a**c**quit, **c**zar, mus**c**le, s**c**issors, Conne**c**ticut, Tu**c**son

D – gran**d**son, We**d**nesday han**d**some, han**d**kerchief, lan**d**scape, san**d**wich (some people pronounce the 'd')

E – We saw the silent 'e' in the Magic 'e' Silent 'e' lesson. We also have silent 'e' in: Wedn**e**sday, veg**e**table...

G – ali**g**n, champa**g**ne, diaphra**g**m, hi**g**h, rei**g**n, forei**g**n...
-**igh**- alight, right, light, eight, weight
-**ugh**- though, through, thought, drought

H – **h**our, honour/honor, honest, heir choir, exhaust, herb (American), exhibition, ghost, rhyme, rhythm, thyme, Thames, Gandhi, Birmingham

I – business

J (none)

K – knead, knell, knickers, knife, knight, knock, knot, know, Knox, Knowles...

L – calf, calm, chalk, folk, half, psalm, salmon, talk, yolk, Norfolk, should, could, would...

M – **m**nemonic

N – autumn, column, condemn, damn, hymn, solemn

O – col_onel, people, leopard

P – corps, coup, pneumonia, pseudo, psychology, receipt, Thompson

Q (none)

R – butter, finger, garden, here (in British English, all r's are 'silent' before consonants)

S – aisle, bourgeois, debris, fracas, island, isle, viscount, Illinois...

T – asthma, ballet, castle, gourmet, listen, rapport, ricochet, soften, thistle, Christmas, tsunami...

U – catalogue, colleague, dialogue, guess, guest, guide, guilt, guitar, tongue

V (none)

W – answer, sword, two, whole, wrist, writ, write, Norwich, Greenwich

X – faux *faux pas, Sioux*

Y (none)

Z – laissez-faire, rendezvous, chez

(You can listen to the pronunciation of these words on the Oxford and the Macmillan online dictionary sites – see the Book and Website Recommendations)

Exercise

1. Britain is __ nown for its music.

2. Reading and ___riting.

3. We read __salms and sing hymns in church.

4. Stop _nashing your teeth!

5. __rap up warm in winter.

6. In summer there are lots of __nats in the countryside.

7. General ___nowledge.

8. ___nives and forks.

9. I'd like to __rite better.

10. I don't _now how to do it.

11. The yo__k of an egg.

12. Autum__ leaves.

13. Brush and com__.

14. Ta___king in your sleep.

15. Fas__en your seatbelt.

16. Lis__en to me!

17. My hands are num__ with cold.

18. Add up this colum___ of figures.

Exercise   Answers

1. Britain is <u>known</u> for its music.

2. Reading and <u>writing</u>.

3. We read <u>psalms</u> and sing hymns in church.

4. Stop <u>gnashing</u> your teeth!

5.   <u>Wrap</u> up warm in winter.

6. In summer there are lots of <u>gnats</u> in the countryside.

7. General <u>knowledge</u>.

8.   <u>Knives</u> and forks.

9. I'd like to <u>write</u> better.

10. I don't <u>know</u> how to do it.

11. The <u>yolk</u> of an egg.

12. <u>Autumn</u> leaves.

13. Brush and <u>comb</u>.

14. <u>Talking</u> in your sleep.

15. <u>Fasten</u> your seatbelt.

16. <u>Listen</u> to me!

17. My hands are <u>numb</u> with cold.

18. Add up this <u>column</u> of figures.

British English vs. American English

color/colour, centre/center, realise/realize

Why are there differences between British and American spellings?

Knowing the differences between American and British English is important due to the Internet and computer software. Also, a lot of computers are automatically set to an American dictionary and will leave you wondering why the spelling has a red squiggly line under it, even though you spelt it correctly!

Knowing the differences adds another layer to your spelling knowledge and stops potential confusion.

There are spelling differences because of the American Revolution. With the Declaration of Independence in 1776, Americans wanted to proclaim their differences from Britain and one way was to reform spelling. Noah Webster led the way. His really radical proposals had little support, but he managed to reform some spellings.

British to American

-our to *-or* — *col**our*** to *col**or***

-re to *-er* — *centre* to *center*

-ise to *-ize* — *realise* to *realize*

-ogue to *-og* **or** *-ogue* — *dialogue* to *dialog* or *dialogue*

No doubling of the final 'l' — *travelling* to *traveling*

-ise or –ize

| realise / realize, apologise / apologize |

Which one do you use? Do you know which is the American ending and which we can use in British English?

As you can see from the table below, British English can use both endings but American English can't. Canadians can use both endings too.

British English -ise or ize	American English -ize
realise or realize	realize
apologise or apologize	apologize
organise or organize	organize
recognise or recognize	recognise or recognize
finalise or finalize	finalize

According to the *Oxford Dictionary*, both endings are correct in British English but only one way in American. They recommend you choose one style and stick to it within a piece of writing.

The *Oxford Dictionary* use the –**ize** ending on their website, maybe because the -**ize** ending is older and closer to its Greek roots. But –**ise** is more widely used.

Drop the 'e' rule: *realising/realizing, finalised/finalized, organisation/organization, recognisable/recognizable…*

CAREFUL – a few words must only be spelled with –**ise**: *advertise, advise, chastise, compromise, despise, devise, disguise, excise, exercise, improvise, promise.*

British *-or* vs. *-our* American

behaviour — behavior

colour — color

demeanour — demeanor

endeavour — endeavor

favourite — favorite

flavour — flavor

glamour — glamor or *glamour**

harbour — harbor

honour — honor

humour — humor

labour — labor

neighbour — neighbor

odour — odor

rumour — rumor

saviour — savior

savoury — savory

splendour — splendor

British **-re** vs. **-er** American

centre — center

centimetre — centimeter

fibre — fiber

kilometre — kilometer

litre — liter

manoeuvre — maneuver

meagre — meager

metre — meter

but *meter* (measuring equipment)

millimetre — millimeter

sombre — somber

theatre — theater or *theatre*

British -**ogue** vs. -**og** or -**ogue** American

British	American
analogue	analog
dialogue	dialog/dialogue
catalogue	catalog/catalogue
epilogue	epilog/epilogue
monologue	monolog/monologue
prologue	prolog/prologue
travelogue	travelog/travelogue
synagogue	synagog/synagogue

British double L with vowel prefixes: — **But not in most American words:**

traveller	traveler
cancelled	canceled
counsellor	counselor
equalled	equaled
fuelling	fueling
grovelling	groveling
jewellery	jewelry
marvellous	marvelous
modelling	modeling
quarrelling	quarreling
woollen	woolen

BUT be careful of these words:

British	American
appal	appall
distil	distill
enrol	enroll
enthral	entrall
fulfil	fulfill
instil	instill
skilful	skillful
wilful	willful

American words vs. British words

licorice — liquorice

maneuver — manoeuvre

plow — plough

sulfur — sulphur

naught — nought

skeptic — sceptic

disk — disc

curb — kerb

vial — phial

whiskey — whisky

jewelry — jewellery

program — programme

(but *computer program*)

In most cases American words have fewer letters.

Exercise

Do you know the British spellings of these American ones?

write a check _____

cozy _____

donut _____

roadside curb _____

mustache _____

omelet _____

pajamas _____

tire _____

gray_____

Exercise   Answers

In most cases American words have fewer letters.

Am – write a check
Br – cheque

Am – cozy
Br – cosy

Am – donut
Br – doughnut (*donut* is becoming a popular spelling in UK)

Am – roadside curb
Br – kerb

Am – mustache
Br – moustache

Am – omelet
Br – omelette

Am – pajamas
Br – pyjamas

Am – tire
Br – tyre

Am – gray
Br – grey

Consolidation / Revision Section

write / writing / written / wrote

> *I'm **writing** to complain about the letter you **wrote** asking for information that I've already **written** to you about.*

Lots of people mistakenly double up the 't' in *writing* (~~writting~~ x) *or keep the 'e'* ~~writeing~~ x

write is a verb: *to write, I write, she writes...*

Notice the 'i' is a long vowel sound. This is because of the silent 'e' at the end of the word – writ**e**. **Writing** also has a long vowel sound.

writing = write + "drop the 'e' with **–ing**" = **writing**

We also drop the 'e' with -**able** in *writable*, a *rewritable* DVD

The past tense of *write* is **wrote**: *I wrote, you wrote, she wrote, he wrote...* Notice again the silent 'e' makes the vowel long and say its alphabet name "oh".

writ is a short sound, so when we double the 't' and add –**en** it makes *written*. 'i' remains a short vowel sound.

Written is a past particle - *I've written to the bank. She's written. They've written to me.*

It's also an adjective - the *written* word, *written* records.

So we have a long vowel sound for **write,** and when we add -**ing** we drop the 'e' to make **writing.**

We have a short vowel sound in **writ** and double up the 't' to make **written**

Remember double letters after a vowel usually indicate a short vowel sound which helps with reading, spelling, and speaking.

But when we add a vowel suffix we double up the end consonant to keep the short vowel sound:
put – putting
sit – sitter
jog – jogging
quiz – quizzical
writ – written

Flossy words
Double letters dropped out of fashion at the end of most words except with some words ending in **f, l, s**
floss, moss, toss, gloss, glass, mass, fuss, mess
fill, bill, hill, fell, bell, hell, full, bull, hull
cuff, huff, stuff, scuff, scoff

We just add suffixes to these words:
flossing, scuffed, felled, billing, scoffed, messed, messy

quit / quite / quiet

> I **quit** my job because it was **quite** stressful, and now my life is **quiet**.

1. Which ones have one syllable?

2. Which one has two syllables?

3. Which one means to stop doing something?

4. Which one means be silent, silence, "shush!"

5. Which one means fairly or very?

6. Which one is an adverb?

7. Which one is a verb?

8. Which one is an adjective?

Answers

1. Which ones have one syllable? **quit / quite**
2. Which one has two syllables? **quiet**
3. Which one means to stop doing something? **quit**
4. Which one means be silent, silence, "shush!" **quiet**
5. Which one means fairly or very? **quite**
6. Which one is an adverb? **quite**
7. Which one is a verb? **to quit**
8. Which one is an adjective? **quiet**

Quit is a short vowel sound. *I quit smoking. I quit my job.*
- Informal – to leave a job or school permanently: *His decision to quit international football has shocked everyone.*
- Informal – to stop doing something: *She drinks so much, she could never quit now.*
- Formal – to leave a place: notice to quit (=an official order to leave a place within a certain time): *Their landlord has given them notice to quit.*

Quite
quit + **magic 'e'** = **quite** (long vowel sound)
*They're **quite** cute. It's **quite** a hard word to spell.*

There are small meaning differences between British and American English for **quite**

In British English, **quite** usually means 'fairly': *The film was quite enjoyable, although some of the acting was weak.*

When American speakers say **quite**, they usually mean 'very': *We've examined the figures quite thoroughly.*

British English sometimes use **quite** to mean 'very', but only before words with an extreme meaning: *The whole experience was **quite** amazing.*

- fairly but not very: *I was feeling quite tired after our walk.*
- quite a good/big, etc. something: *We had to wait for quite a long time.*
- completely: *Are you quite sure you know what to do?*

quite is a long vowel sound and **quit** is a short vowel sound but they both have one syllable.

Quiet

quiet has two syllables "qu / et"
quiet = Shush! Be quiet.

Please be quiet.
I love the peace and quiet of the countryside.
All I want is a quiet life.

One way to remember the spelling, or the right usage, is to pronounce and exaggerate the syllables in **quiet** "qu / et" "k / why / et"

Exercise

Write in **quit, quite,** or **quiet**

a. All I want is a _____ life.

b. I wish she would _____ smoking.

c. If I had the money I would _____ my job.

d. It's _____ a hard word to spell and I'm not _____ sure how to spell it.

e. Their landlord has given them a notice to _____.

f. The view was _____ amazing.

g. Will you please be _____!

Exercise   Answers

a. All I want is a **quiet** life.

b. I wish she would **quit** smoking.

c. If I had the money I would **quit** my job.

d. It's **quite** a hard word to spell and I'm not **quite** sure how to spell it.

e. Their landlord has given them a notice to **quit**.

f. The view was **quite** amazing.

g. Will you please be **quiet**!

Revision Exercise

Find all the 8 mistakes and underline them, then copy the letter with the corrections.

Hi Karen

The reason I'm writting is I'm haveing a party on Wenesday for Mike's 60th birthday. I'm paniccing, so I was wonderring if you could help me with the shoping and makeing a cake.

Let me no if that's OK.

Lisa

Hi Karen

_____

_____

_____

_____

_____

Lisa

Revision Exercise Answers

Hi Karen

The reason I'm <u>writing</u> is I'm <u>having</u> a party on
Wednesday for Mike's 60th birthday. I'm <u>panicking,</u>
so I was <u>wondering</u> if you could help me with the
<u>shopping</u> and <u>making</u> a cake.

Let me <u>know</u> if that's OK.

Lisa

Exercise

Adding -**ing** and -**ed**

Spell these words with -**ing** and -**ed**. Use your knowledge of spelling rules to complete the task.

1. shop _____ _____

2. slim _____ _____

3. rain _____ _____

4. please _____ _____

5. celebrate _____ _____

6. agree _____ _____

7. apply _____ _____

8. prefer _____ _____

9. phone _____ _____

10. repeat _____ _____

11. write _____ _____

Exercise Answers
Adding -ing and -ed

Spell these words with **-ing** and **-ed**. Use your knowledge of spelling rules to complete the task.

1. shop <u>shopping</u> <u>shopped</u> (double up)

2. slim <u>slimming</u> <u>slimmed</u> (double up)

3. rain <u>raining</u> <u>rained</u> (no change)

4. please <u>pleasing</u> <u>pleased</u> (drop 'e')

5. celebrate <u>celebrating</u> <u>celebrated</u> (drop 'e')

6. agree <u>agreeing</u> <u>agreed</u>

7. apply <u>applying</u> <u>applied</u>

8. prefer <u>preferring</u> <u>preferred</u>

9. phone <u>phoning</u> <u>phoned</u>

10. repeat <u>repeating</u> <u>repeated</u>

11. write <u>writing</u> <u>wrote</u> (irregular past tense)

Exercise
Rewrite and add the correct "shun" ending (-tion, -sion, -cian)

a. direct _____

b. music _____

c. include _____

d. complete _____

e. permit _____

f. intrude _____

g. process _____

h. optic _____

i. reduce _____

j. impress _____

k. operate _____

l. electric _____

Exercise   Answers

Rewrite and add the correct "shun" ending (-tion, -sion, -cian)

a. direct <u>direction</u>

b. music <u>musician</u>

c. include <u>inclusion</u>

d. complete <u>completion</u>

e. permit <u>permission</u>

f. intrude <u>intrusion</u>

g. process <u>procession</u>

h. optic <u>optician</u>

i. reduce <u>reduction</u>

j. impress <u>impression</u>

k. operate <u>operation</u>

l. electric <u>electrician</u>

Exercise

Rewrite and add -**able** to make adjectives

a. imagine _____

b. change _____

c. rely _____

d. unforget _____

e. pleasure _____

f. achieve _____

g. unstop _____

h. manage _____

i. excite _____

j. notice _____

k. argue _____

l. regret _____

m. dispose _____

n. recharge _____

Exercise   Answers

Rewrite and add -**able** to make adjectives

a. imagine <u>unimaginable</u> (drop the 'e')

b. change <u>changeable</u> (keep the 'e')

c. rely <u>reliable</u> ('y' to 'i')

d. unforget <u>unforgettable</u> (double 't')

e. pleasure <u>pleasurable</u>

f. achieve <u>achievable</u>

g. unstop <u>unstoppable</u>

h. manage <u>manageable</u>

i. excite <u>excitable</u>

j. notice <u>noticeable</u>

k. argue <u>arguable</u>

l. regret <u>regrettable</u>

m. dispose <u>disposable</u>

n. recharge <u>rechargeable</u>

Exercice

The missing words all end with **-ible**. Use the clues to complete the words.

a. It's easy to get to - it's easily ac_____

b. This is so bendy and fl_____

c. His behaviour was so reckless and ir_____
   behavior (AmE)

c. It cannot be resisted it's totally ir_____

d. The story sounds likely and very pl_____

e. Deckchairs are c_____ and fold away.

Exercise   Answers

The missing words all end with **-ible**. Use the clues to complete the words.

a. It's easy to get to - it's easily <u>accessible</u>

b. This is so bendy and <u>flexible</u>

c. His behaviour was so reckless and <u>irresponsible</u>
        behavior (AmE)

c. It cannot be resisted it's totally <u>irresistible</u>

d. The story sounds likely and very <u>plausible</u>

e. Deckchairs are <u>collapsible</u> and fold away.

Exercise

Write in the plurals. Use your understanding of plural rules to complete the task.

For example: She bought two new _____ (dress)
                      She bought two new <u>dresses</u> (dress)

1. Shopping list:

   _____ (tomato)
   _____ (potato)
   _____ (strawberry)
   _____ (banana)
   _____ (peach)

2. Her dog gave birth to 4 _____ (puppy)

3. This weekend, they're visiting 3 _____ (city)

4. At the end of emails I usually write:
   Best _____ (wish)

5. My kids love listening to _____ (story)

6. To get to work, he has to catch 2 _____ (bus)

Exercise Answers

Write in the plurals. Use your understanding of spelling rules to complete the task.

For example: She bought two new _____ (dress)
She bought two new <u>dresses</u> (dress)

1. Shopping list:
<u>tomatoes</u> (tomato)
<u>potatoes</u> (potato)
<u>strawberries</u> (strawberry)
<u>bananas</u> (banana)
<u>peaches</u> (peach)

2. Her dog gave birth to 4 <u>puppies.</u> (puppy)

3. This weekend, they're visiting 3 <u>cities.</u> (city)

4. At the end of emails I usually write:
Best <u>wishes</u> (wish)

5. My kids love listening to <u>stories.</u> (story)

6. To get to work, he has to catch 2 <u>buses.</u> (bus)

Exercise

Use the prefixes and suffixes below and make as many words as you can from the root word.

Prefixes: **dis re un   ap**
Suffixes: **ed ful   able   ly   al   er**

colour:
color (AmE):

cover:

claim:

prove:

Possible answers

colour: discolour, discoloured, uncoloured, colourful,
colourfully
color (AmE): discolor, discolored, uncolored, colorful,
colorfully

cover: discover, discovered, recover, recovered, recoverable,
unrecoverable, covered

claim: disclaim, disclaimer, reclaim, reclaimed, unclaimed,
reclaimable, claimable

prove: disprove, disproved, reprove, unproved, approved,
approval, disapproval, provable, disapproving

Exercise
Use the suffixes below and make as many
words as you can from the root word.

Suffixes: **ed ing able s ent**

study

achieve

healthy

Use the suffixes below and make as many
words as you can from the root word.

Suffixes: **ed ing able s ent**

Possible answers

study: studying, studied, studies, student

achieve: achieving, achieved, achieves, achievable,
achievement

require: requiring, required, requires, requirements

Exercise

Rewrite and add the vowel suffixes in **bold** to the root words

a. (**er**) begin _____

b. (**ing**) picnic _____

c. (**en**) forbid _____

d. (**ed**) permit _____

e. (**ing**) regret _____

f. (**ing**) budget _____

g. (**ed**) panic _____

h. (**ed**) equip _____

i. (**ing**) write _____

j. (**ing**) study _____

Exercise   Answers

Rewrite and add the vowel suffixes in **bold** to the root words

a. (**er**) begin   <u>beginner</u>

b. (**ing**) picnic   <u>picnicking</u>

c. (**en**) forbid   <u>forbidden</u>

d. (**ed**) permit   <u>permitted</u>

e. (**ing**) regret   <u>regretting</u>

f. (**ing**) budget   <u>budgeting</u> (stress on first syllable!)

g. (**ed**) panic   <u>panicked</u>

h. (**ed**) equip   <u>equipped</u>

i. (**ing**) write   <u>writing</u>

j. (**ing**) study   <u>studying</u>

Exercise -ous/-able/-ible revision

Write the synonym/similar word for the word shown in **bold**

a. It's a **beautiful** day / It's a _g_____ day.

b. That joke was very **funny**, it was _hil_____._

c. Her goal was **possible** /
   Her goal was _ach_____._

d. That was a **stupid** idea utterly _rid_____._

e. He's very **worried** about something /
   He's _anx_____._

f. It's **unreadable** - totally _ill_____._

 g. It comes in **different** sizes /
   It comes in _v_____ sizes.

Exercise   Answers

Write the synonym/similar word for the word shown in **bold**

a. It's a **beautiful** day / It's a gorgeous day.

b. That joke was very **funny**, it was hilarious

c. Her goal was **possible** /
    Her goal was achievable

d. That was a **stupid** idea utterly ridiculous.

e. He's very **worried** about something /
    He's anxious about something.

f. It's **unreadable** - totally illegible.

g. It comes in **different** sizes /
    It comes in various sizes.

Exercise

Add **-ous** to these words

1. continue _____

2. vary _____

3. mischief _____

4. marvel _____

5. adventure _____

6. fury _____

7. rebel _____

8. nerve _____

9. outrage _____

10. ridicule _____

Exercise   Answers

Add **–ous** to these words

1. continue - <u>continuous</u>

2. vary - <u>various</u>

3. mischief - <u>mischievous</u>

4. marvel - marvellous or marvelous (AmE)

5. adventure - <u>adventurous</u>

6. fury - <u>furious</u>

7. rebel - <u>rebellious</u>

8. nerve - <u>nervous</u>

9. outrage - <u>outrageous</u>

10. ridicule - <u>ridiculous</u>

Proofreading Exercise

Think about the suffix rules and rewrite this passage, correcting the mistakes. (19 mistakes). Can you see what doesn't look right? Do some of these spelling look strange?

For centurys scientists have been commited to solveing problems for the purpose of benefitting mankind. In earlyer days they had little equippment but still made many amazeing discoverys. When factorys first openned, safty was not a major concern, but as people became more qualifyed, a more careing environment developped. These days supplyes of servicable goods are plentyful and the old days of dangerous working conditions are eassly forgoten.

Thanks to Shireen Shuster's *Spelling Essentials* book

Proofreading Exercise Answers

Think about the suffix rules and rewrite this passage, correcting the mistakes. (19 mistakes). Can you see what doesn't look right? Do some of these spelling look strange?

For **centuries** scientists have been **committed** to **solving** problems for the purpose of **benefiting** mankind. In **earlier** days they had little **equipment** but still made many **amazing discoveries**. When **factories** first **opened**, **safety** was not a major concern, but as people became more **qualified**, a more **caring** environment **developed**. These days **supplies** of **serviceable** goods are **plentiful** and the old days of dangerous working conditions are **easily forgotten**.

Thanks to Shireen Shuster's *Spelling Essentials* book

Self-assessment

Remember this from the beginning of the book?

DO NOT beat yourself up if you can't remember - these rules take time to get them in your long-term memory, so go back to the lessons and recap.

1. Why do we double some consonants with suffixes? For example, *putting,* but not *seat – seating.*

2. Why do we have double/single letters before **-le?**
   giggle but not *Google*
   apple   but not *maple*
   puddle but not *poodle*

3. Why do we write **-ck**, **-k** or **-ke** at the end of words when they sound the same? For *example, luck, cook, make.*

4. Why do we keep the 'e' in *manageable* and *noticeable*?

5. Why are these spellings wrong?
   a. truely   b. haveing   c. writting

6. Do we write wonderfull or wonderful?

7. What's the difference between **hoping** and **hopping** and why do we double up the 'p'?

Self-assessment Answers

1. Why do we double some consonants with suffixes?
    For example, *put - putting, shop - shopping, begin – beginner*, but not *seat - seating, rain – raining...*

This is the 1:1:1 doubling up rule. We double the last consonant when there is 1 syllable + 1 vowel next to 1 end consonant. Double consonants indicate a short vowel sound.

2. Why do we have double/single letters before –**le**?
    giggle   but not *Google*
    apple   but not *maple*
    puddle but not *poodle*

Double the consonant to indicate a short vowel sound.

3. Why do we write –**ck**, –**k** or –**ke** at the end of words when sound the same? For *example, luck, cook, make.*
Again this is about short and long vowel sounds.
'luck' is a short vowel sound so has a –ck ending, 'cook' has two vowels so ends in '-k','make' is a long vowel sound so ends in '-ke'

4. Why do we keep the 'e' in *manageable* and *noticeable* but drop the 'e' with other –able words such as *believable* and *excitable*?
We keep the "e" with "g" and "c" to soften their sounds.

5. Why are these spellings wrong?

        a. *truely*   b. *haveing*   c. *writting*

They're wrong because we need to drop the 'e' with -ing
(b. having c. writing) and drop the 'e' in truly –
true + ly = *truly*.

6. Do we write *wonderfull* or *wonderful*?

When we add the -ful ending, we write '*wonderful*'.
Only use "full" when "full", e.g., *full up, full on*.
We have two 'ls' when we add -ly to -ful: wonderfully,
hopefully

7. What's the difference between *hoping* and ***hopping*** and
why do we double up the 'p'?

hoping = hope + ing (drop the 'e' with -ing and still keep
the long vowel sound)

hopping = hop + p + ing (1:1:1 doubling up rule to keep
the short vowel sound)

~ Go over the lessons again and again.~

Notice spelling rules and their patterns everywhere – on
billboards, ads, newspaper, online...

That's All Folks!

Thank you for taking the time to go through this book and for investing in your learning. Remember to keep going over the rules until you're sure of them. Notice spelling rules and patterns everywhere, and use them in your writing.

Knowing spelling rules is one of many spelling strategies to help you learn, remember and understand spelling. It adds another layer to your knowledge about spelling.

As you've seen, spelling rules are useful to know but there are always exceptions that you need to learn. You may forget the rule but hopefully you'll remember the pattern, or use a memory trick to help you.

For more information on using spelling strategies, memory tricks, spelling tips, exercises and games, go to www.howtospell.co.uk

Further reading: *The Reasons Why English Spelling is so Weird and Wonderful* by Joanne Rudling. A useful, fun look at the history and development of English spelling and why there are some strange spellings. And *How to Spell the 20 Most Commonly Misspelled Words* – available on Amazon and howtospell.co.uk.

For an online course with videos, exercises, pronunciation podcasts and tests, try *Spelling Rules, Patterns and Strategies Masterclass*, available from howtospell.co.uk.

About the Author

Joanne Rudling is an author, freelance lecturer, teacher trainer, and owner of www.howtospell.co.uk, where she's developed online spelling courses for adults.

She's taught spelling, literacy and writing for 18 years in various organizations including: the City of Westminster College, Bournemouth FE College, Dorset Adult Education, Bournemouth University, and Bournemouth Film School (now The Arts University College of Bournemouth).

Joanne has developed and taught on literacy projects for the Pre-Volunteer Programme for the Olympics, and the RNIB (Royal National Institute for the Blind).

She also edits closed captions/sub-titles from American spellings to British for Amazon.com TV drama division.

After overcoming her own spelling, grammar and punctuation problems, Joanne's mission now is to help others to spell and write well.

Other books by Joanne:
How to Spell the 20 Most Commonly Misspelled Words.
QTS Spelling Strategies to Help You Pass the Literacy Skills Spelling Test.
Punctuation Guide and Workbook.
The Reasons Why English Spelling is so Weird and Wonderful.

Available on Amazon and www.howtospell.co.uk

Book and Website Recommendations

Joanne Rudling: *The Reasons Why English Spelling is so Weird and Wonderful*

Joann Rudling: *How to Spell the 20 Most Commonly Misspelled Words* (available from howtospell.co.uk or Amazon)

Shireen Shuster: *Spelling Essentials* (Longman)

Catherine Taylor: *A Useful Spelling Handbook for Adults (Olympia Publishers)*

Joy Pollock: *Signposts to Spelling* (Blessings Book Publishing)

John J. Fulford: *The Complete Guide to English Spelling Rules* (Astoria Press)

The Book of Spelling Rules (Wordsworth Reference)

For Teachers

Johanna Stirling: *Teaching Spelling to English Language Learners* (Amazon) (blog http://thespellingblog.blogspot.co.uk)

Sally Raymond: *Spelling Rules, Riddles and Remedies* (Routledge)

Websites

www.bbc.co.uk/skillswise
www.beatingdyslexia.com
www.howtospell.co.uk

Online Dictionaries

www.oxforddictionaries.com - British & American
www.macmillandictionary.com - British & American
American online dictionary - www.merriam-webster.com